D0519221

FINAL EDITION.

CONCERT VERSION

OF

MERRIE ENGLAND.

WRITTEN BY

BASIL HOOD.

COMPOSED BY

EDWARD GERMAN.

PRICE 15/- NET

Choruses only, S.S.A. Concert Version, PRICE 3/- NET

Choruses only, O.N., Concert Version, PRICE 3/- NET

Choruses only, Tonic Sol-fa, PRICE 3/- NET

CHAPPELL & Co., Ltd.,

50, NEW BOND STREET, LONDON, W.1.

NEW YORK and SYDNEY.

Orchestral Parts may be Hired.

Printed in England.

THE ARGUMENT

THE ARGUMENT, as developed in the Opera (omitting the principal humorous characters and incidents) is that Sir Walter Raleigh is in love with Bessie Throckmorton, one of Queen Elizabeth's Maids of Honour. He writes an acrostic to her, which, being lost, is found by Jill-all-alone, a dweller in the woods, who is suspected of being a witch: she gives it to the Earl of Essex, who, considering Sir Walter Raleigh to be his rival for the hand of Queen Elizabeth, uses it against him by handing it to the Queen. She reads the praises of a certain Bessie, and taking the compliment to herself, is not displeased thereby; when, however, she discovers that the acrostic was intended for her maid (Bessie Throckmorton) she orders Raleigh to be banished and Bessie to be imprisoned. Jill, who has further incensed the Queen by some mocking words, is ordered to be burnt as a witch.

Essex, when he discovers that Raleigh is not his rival, attempts to repair the mischief he has wrought by the following device:—

He arranges that one of the foresters shall impersonate Herne the Hunter and appear in an apparition to the Queen while she is seated in the forest beneath Herne's Oak. According to tradition the appearance of the weird huntsman occurs only when the monarch contemplates a crime. The device succeeds, the Queen relents, and both the lovers and Jill are pardoned.

CONCERT VERSION

— OF —

MERRIE ENGLAND.

CHARACTERS

BESSIE THROCKMORTON (*Maid of Honour to the Queen*)	..	*Soprano*
"JILL-ALL-ALONE" (*a supposed Witch*) / QUEEN ELIZABETH	.. ..	*Contralto*
SIR WALTER RALEIGH	.. ..	*Tenor*
THE EARL OF ESSEX	.. ..	*Baritone*

A TAILOR	.. ..	*Tenor*	*Members of Chorus*
A BAKER	.. ..	*Tenor*	
A TINKER	.. ..	*Baritone*	
*A BUTCHER / LONG TOM	.. ..	*Bass*	

Chorus of LORDS, LADIES, TOWNSFOLK, SOLDIERS, &C.

**These parts may be taken by the same Vocalist.*

CONTENTS.

PART I.

PART II.

MERRIE ENGLAND.

INTRODUCTION.

Allegro con spirito. (♩= 112)
PIANO.
fff Tutti
sff
Silent.
Allegro moderato. ♩= 104.
Strings
mf
p
Timp.
A
Oboe
f
p
f
p
Ped.
Ped.
Ped.
Ped.

f
pp delicato.
Ped.
Tutti
ff
Ob.
Cl.
D
f p
1
2 rit
E
a tempo.
p

f
p
f
Ped.
F delicato
p
f
ppp
Tutti
f
accel.
ff trem.
Prestissimo. ♩. = 200.
Str.
sf
ff Tamb.

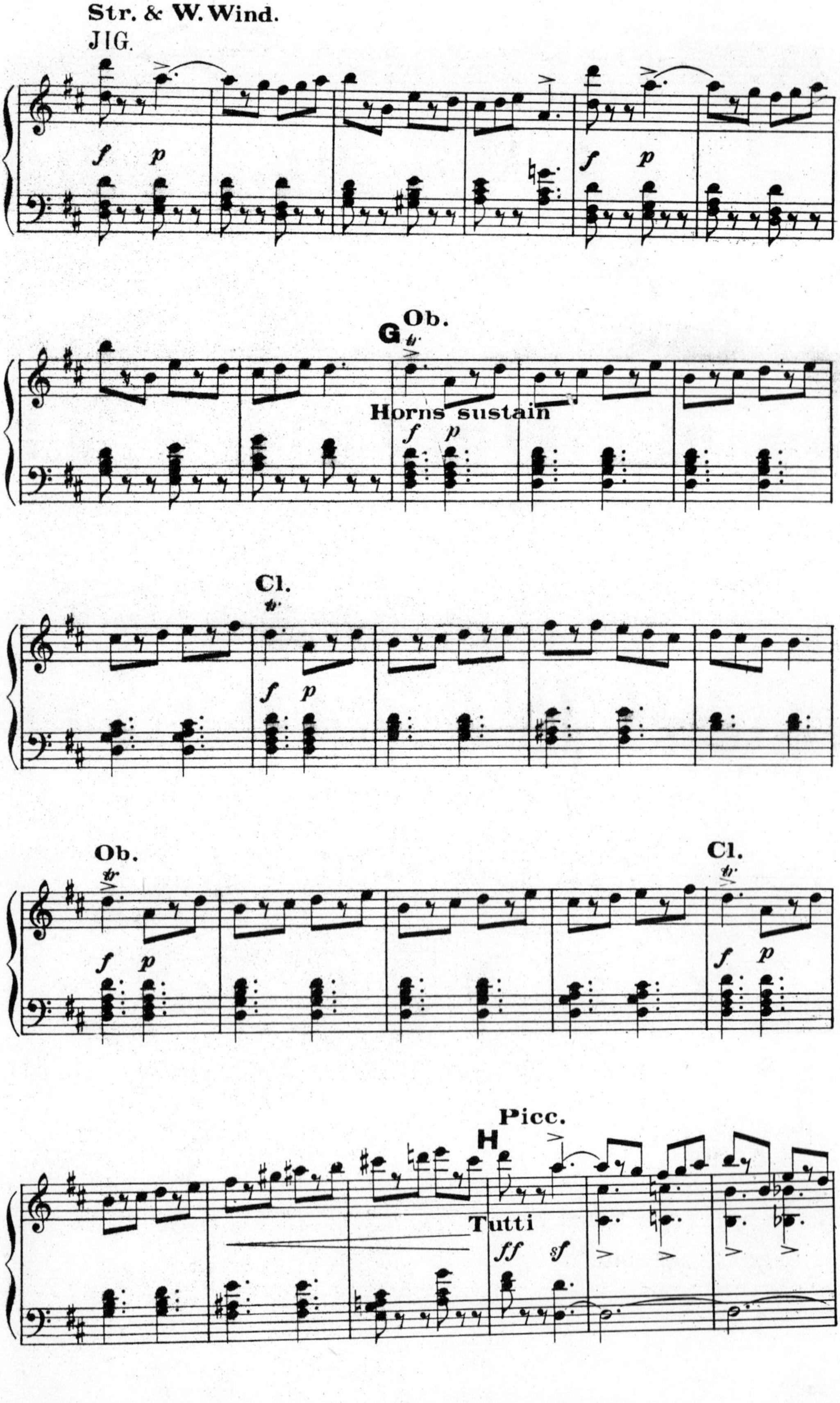
Str. & W. Wind.
JIG.
f p
f p
G Ob.
tr
Horns sustain
f p
Cl.
tr
f p
Ob.
tr
f p
Cl.
tr
f p
Picc.
H
Tutti
ff sf

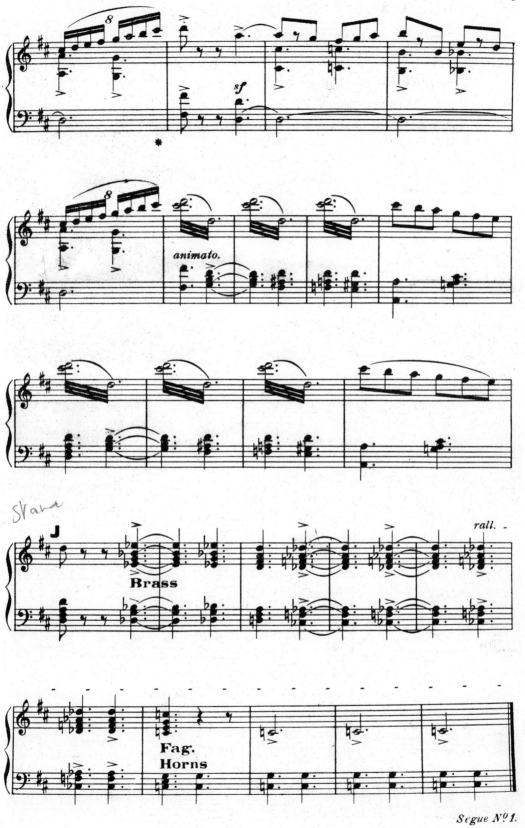

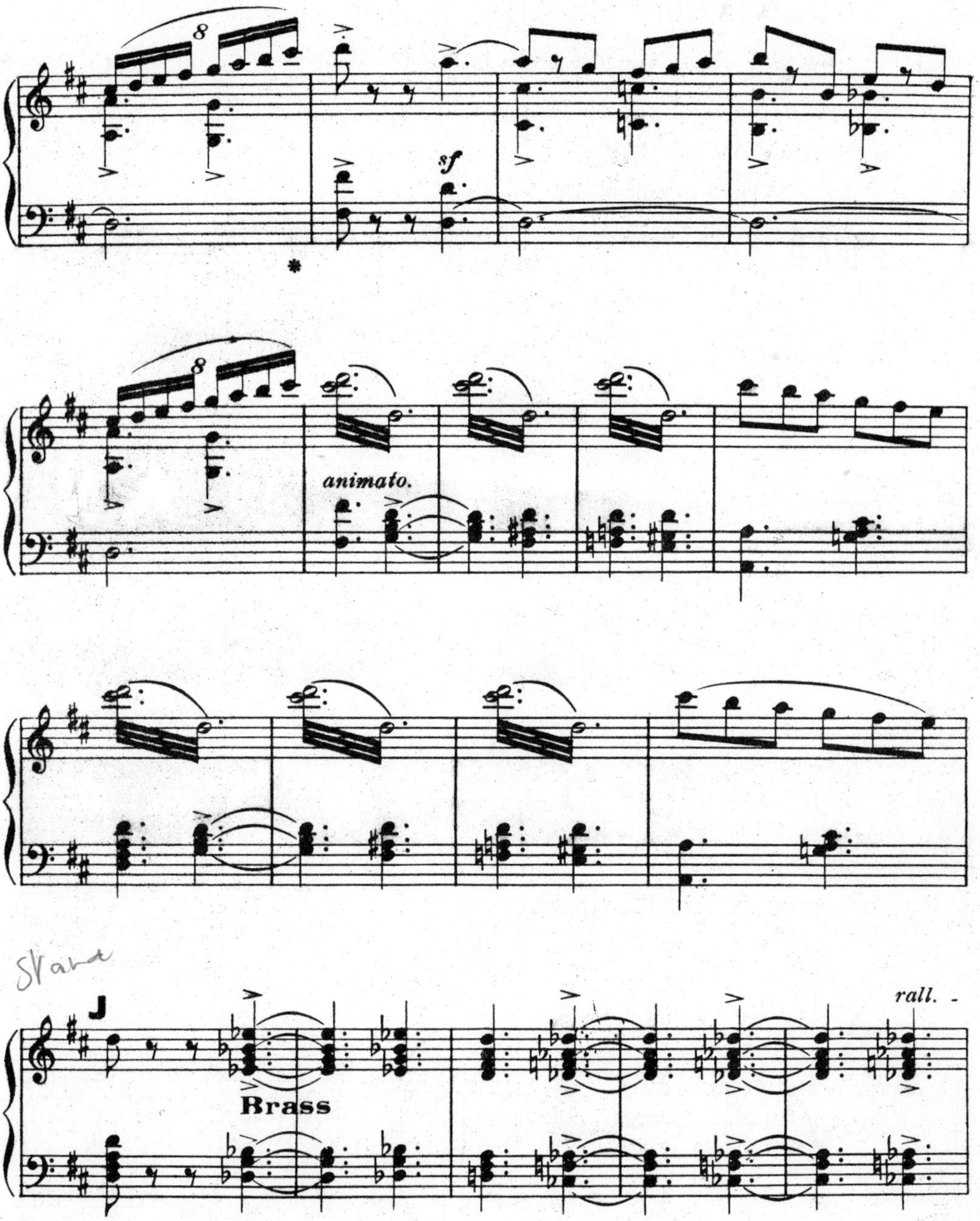
8
sf
8
animato.
J
Brass
rall.
Fag.
Horns

Segue No. 1.

STAND

Nº 1. OPENING CHORUS.

Str. W. W. & Horns
Allegro vivace. ♩. = 132.
p
cresc.
A
Fl.
f
Tutti
sf

Ped.
Ped.
Ped.
Ped.
B
GIRLS.
CHORUS.
Sing a down, a down, a down a, Sing a down, a
MEN.
Sing a down, a down, a down a, Sing a down, a
pizz.
L.H.
CHORUS.
down a, Sing a down, a
down a, Sing a down, a
Tutti L.H.

CHORUS.
down, a down a, Sing a down, a down a.
down, a down a, Sing a down, a down a.
Cl.
CHORUS.
MEN.
Who comes this way?
p
C
Not too fast.
f
CHORUS.
The May Queen comes,
f
The May Queen comes,
Not too fast.
Tutti
f
Timp.

CHORUS.
let her path be spread With ro - ses white and with ro - ses
let her path be spread With ro - ses white and with ro - ses
CHORUS.
red, O, let her path be spread with the flow'rs of Mer - rie
red, O, let her path be spread with the flow'rs of Mer - rie
CHORUS.
Eng - land, of Mer - rie Eng - - land!
Eng - land, of Mer - rie Eng - - land!
Picc.

Animato.
p
Tamb.
D
f Brass
CHORUS.
mf MEN.
Of what shall be the crown For the Queen o' May?
pizz.
Fl.
CHORUS.
p
Of ro - ses
Trumpets
Cl.
Str.
p dolce.
Horns
Ped.
*
Fag.

red ___ We'll make a crown
white and of ro - ses red, We'll make ___ a crown for the
CHORUS.
Ped. * Ped. * Ped. * Ped. * Ped. *
May Queen's head, For the May Queen's head.
CHORUS.
p
Of ro - ses
Fl.
Ped. *
p
Of ro - ses white and ro - ses red, The flowr's of
CHORUS.
white and ro - ses red, The flowr's of
Brass

CHORUS.
Eng-land, of Eng-land, the flow'rs of Mer-rie Eng - land!
Eng-land, of Eng-land, the flow'rs of Mer-rie Eng - land!
CHORUS.
E
And who shall guard the crown of the Queen o'
pizz.
CHORUS.
May?
Fl.
Trumpets
Cl.

CHORUS.
MEN.
bred, Who wear her
Two men of Wind - sor born and bred, Who wear her
Str.
Ped. * Ped. * Ped. * Ped. * Ped. *
CHORUS.
bad - ges of white and red, The flow'rs of Mer-rie Mer-rie Eng - -
bad - ges of white and red, The flow'rs of Mer-rie Mer-rie Eng - -
Brass.
Ped. * Ped. *
CHORUS.
-land, The flow'rs of Mer-rie Mer-rie Eng - - land, of
-land, The flow'rs of Mer-rie Mer-rie Eng - - land, of

F
CHORUS.
Eng - land!
Eng - land!
Fl.
Cl.
f
Timp.
CHORUS.
GIRLS.
The
MEN.
f
The May Queen comes!
Brass
sf
CHORUS.
May Queen comes!
rall.
Ah!
Ah!
rall.

CHORUS.
ff a tempo.
The May Queen comes! let her path be spread With
ff
The May Queen comes! let her path be spread With
Tutti
f a tempo. moderato
Ped. *
ro - ses white And with ro - ses red, O, let her path be
ro - ses white And with ro - ses red, O, let her path be
spread With the flow'rs of Mer-rie Eng - land, of Mer-rie Eng - -
spread With the flow'rs of Mer-rie Eng - land, of Mer-rie Eng - -

G
CHORUS.
-land! TENS.
mf
-land! O, let her path with flow'rs be spread, With ro - ses white and
Picc.
ten.
mf
ten.
CHORUS.
Of Eng - land, of Eng - land, The flow'rs of Mer-rie Eng - land, With
ro-ses red Of Eng - land, of Eng - land, The flow'rs of Mer-rie Eng - land, With
CHORUS.
cresc.
ff
ro - ses white and ro - ses red, The
cresc.
ff
ro - ses white and ro - ses red, The
Tutti
cresc.
Ped.

CHORUS.
flow'rs of Mer - rie Eng - land, The flow'rs of
flow'rs of Eng - land, The flow'rs of
Timp.
H
Molto allegro.
Mer - rie Eng - land!
Mer - rie Eng - land!
Molto allegro.
accel.
Segue.

To P44

No. 2. SONG.- (Jill) and CHORUS.

"OH! WHERE THE DEER DO LIE!"

Allegro. ♩.=104.
Tutti
Str.
f
rall.
Meno mosso. ♩=96.
JILL.
Oh! where the Deer do lie There dwell I,
Fl. (trem.) Cl.
p
Far in the for-est shade, Down— in a dap-pled glade, Ah!— where the Deer do lie,—

Allegro.
There dwell I.
Oh! what a life,
Throw her a bone,
accel.
Brass
rit.
A
No-bo-dy's wife,
Ah!
Jill_ all_ a - lone!
Allegro.
CHORUS.
Oh! what a life,
Oh! what a life,
Str.
rit.
accel.
rall.
Allegro agitato.
Jill,_ all_ a - lone,
CHORUS.
Throw her a bone,
No-bo-dy's wife,
Jill,
Jill.
Throw her a bone,
No-bo-dy's wife,
Jill,
Jill.
Allegro agitato.
rall.
Cymbal

Meno mosso. Cl.
JILL.
B
Where Herne the Hun-ter rides
Str.
trem.
pizz.
ff
sf p
pp
pizz.
Jill a-bides; I hear the ghost-ly sounds, Herne's Phan-tom horn and hounds, Where
f
Herne the hun-ter rides Jill a-bides.
accel.
Allegro.
Oh! she's a witch, Pick up a stone! Die in a ditch,
sf
p

rit.
C
accel.
Ah! Jill, all a - lone.
rit.
p
accel.
Brass.
Allegro.
CHORUS.
ff
Oh! she's a witch! Pick up a stone!
ff
Oh! she's a witch! Pick up a stone!
ENCORE.
ff
Meno mosso.
JILL.
Fl.
But when the morn - ing breaks And a-wakes all o-ther for-est
Str.
sf
pp
Cl.
animato
things, Jill, too, a - wakes, a -

(Beat 6.)
rit.
D f largamente
-wakes and sings. Oh! the sweet day, Queen on a throne,
rit.
f colla voce
(Beat 2.)
p accel.
mer-ry as May, mer-ry as May.
p accel.
f
largamente
ff rall.
molto
Presto.
Jill all a-lone.
CHORUS.
Jill all a-lone.
rall.
ff
molto
Jill all a-lone.
Tutti
largamente
Presto.
pizz. arco
ff rall. molto
sf sf sf

No 3. SONG.- (Raleigh) and CHORUS.

"THAT EVERY JACK."

(BAND PARTS in B♭)

Allegro spiritoso. ♩=108.
ENCORE.
Tutti
f
sf
pizz.
rall.
pizz.
RALEIGH.
1. That ev - - 'ry Jack should have a Jill Dame
2. Jack will lay you on the ground If
sf a tempo
p
pizz.
Na - ture al - ways meant, sirs; But
you stay long to - geth - er; For
CHORUS.
p.
Dame Na - ture al - ways meant, sirs;
If you stay long to - geth - er;
p.
Dame Na - ture al - ways meant, sirs;
If you stay long to - geth - er;
arco
ten. pp
S. Drum.

where's the gill can hope to fill This Jack to his con-
I'll be bound, tho' fat and round, He is as tough as
pizz.
Ped.
A
-tent, sirs? Since three
lea - ther! And who
p
Black Jack to his con - tent, sirs.
He is as tough as lea - ther.
p
Black Jack to his con - tent, sirs.
He is as tough as lea - ther.
Brass
arco
ten. pp
Ped. S. Drum.
or four of gills, or more, Do make his pro-per mea-sure; Give
so wills to steal his Jills Will find it is a tus - sle, Till
pp

Jack his mead And Jack in-deed, Will bub-ble high, Will
on his back he's laid by Jack, For Jack's a man, For
Fl.
Ped. *
bub-ble high with plea - sure!
Jack's a man of mus - cle!
p
accel. e cresc.
Will bub-ble high, will
For Jack's a man, for
p
Will bub-ble high, will
For Jack's a man, for
f
p
Timp.
Ah!
Ah!
f
bub - ble high, will bub - ble high with plea - sure.
Jack's a man, for Jack's a man of mus - cle.
f
bub - ble high, will bub - ble high with plea - sure.
Jack's a man, for Jack's a man of mus - cle.
sff

B
rall.
a tempo
Then here's a lack Of care that kills, When ev-'ry Jack Hath
But here's a lack Of care that kills, When ev-'ry Jack Hath
Brass
f
fp
all his gills Of what he wills, Or mead, or sack, For they're the Jills For
all his gills Of what he wills, Or mead, or sack, For they're the Jills For
Fag.
sf
fat Black Jack!
fat Black Jack!
Then here's a lack of care that kills, When
But here's a lack of care that kills, When
Then here's a lack of care that kills, When
But here's a lack of care that kills, When
Tutti

C
ev - 'ry Jack Hath all his gills Of what he wills, Of mead, or
ev - 'ry Jack Hath all his gills Of what he wills, Of mead, or
ev - 'ry Jack Hath all his gills Of what he wills, Of mead, or
ev - 'ry Jack Hath all his gills Of what he wills, Of mead, or.
For they're the Jills, For they're the Jills for fat Black
For they're the Jills, For they're the Jills for fat Black
sack, For they're the Jills, For they're, they're the Jills for fat Black
sack, For they're the Jills, For they're, they're the Jills for fat Black
sack, For they're the Jills, For they're, they're the Jills for fat Black
sack, For they're the Jills, For they're, they're the Jills for fat Black
sf

1.
Jack.
Jack.
Jack.
pizz.
sf rall.
pizz.
2.
2. Now Jack for fat Black
Jack For they're the jills for fat Black
Jack For they're the jills for fat Black
f
accel.
Jack.
Jack.
Jack.
accel.
Tutti

No. 4. QUINTET.

"LOVE IS MEANT TO MAKE US GLAD."

(BAND PARTS in F.)

(Not too fast.)
Allegretto grazioso. ♩= 96.
Str.
Cl. (sus.)
p
Not too fast.
BESSIE.
p
pp
Love is meant to make us glad– Hey jol-ly, jol-ly, Hey
JILL.
p
pp
Love is meant to make us glad– Hey ho!
RALEIGH.
p
pp
Love is meant to make us glad– Hey jol-ly, jol-ly, Hey
ESSEX.
p
pp
Love is meant to make us glad– Hey ho!
LONG TOM.
p
pp
Love is meant to make us glad– Hey ho!
Not too fast.
Fl.
p
pp
pizz.

B.
J.
R.
ES.
L.T.
pp
jol-ly lit-tle Cu-pid! Fools do let him make them sad! Hey fol-ly, fol-ly, Hey
Hey ho! Fools do let him make them sad! Hey ho!
jol-ly lit-tle Cu-pid! Fools do let him make them sad! Hey fol-ly, fol-ly, Hey
Hey ho! Fools do let him make them sad! Hey ho!
Hey ho! Fools do let him make them sad! Hey ho!
mf
fol-ly, they are stu-pid! Let's be wise If we do meet him!
hey ho! Let's be wise If we do meet him!
fol-ly, they are stu-pid!
hey ho! Let's be wise If we do meet him!
hey ho! Let's be wise
Ob.
Hrn.

B.
J.
R.
ES.
L.T.
Ah!
Let's be wise, Let's be wise, Oh
Ah!
Let's be wise, Let's be wise, Oh
Heave no sighs But glad-ly greet him! Let's be wise, Let's be wise, Oh
Heave no sighs But glad-ly greet him! Let's be wise, Let's be wise, Oh
Heave no sighs But glad-ly greet him! Let's be wise, Let's be wise, Oh
A animato
Love is meant to make us glad, is meant to make us glad!
Love is meant to make us glad, to make us glad!
Love is meant to make us glad, to make us glad!
Love is meant to make us glad, is meant to make us glad!
Love is meant to make us glad, to make us glad!
W.W.
animato
Timp.

B.
J.
R.
ES.
L.T.
f
p
And say to him "Good day" to him, He'll treat us as we
And say to him "Good day" to him, He'll treat us as we
And say to him "Good day" to him, He'll treat us as we
And say to him "Good day" to
And say to him "Good day" to
treat him! With a hey, jol-ly, jol-ly, hey,
treat him! He'll treat us as we treat him!
treat him! With a hey, jol-ly jol-ly, hey,
him!
him! He'll treat us as we treat him!
mf

B.
jol-ly, lit-tle Love! Hey, lit-tle Love! With a hey, jol-ly, jol-ly, hey,
J.
Hey! With a hey,
R.
jol-ly, lit-tle Love! Hey! With a hey,
ES.
Hey! With a hey,
L.T.
Hey! With a hey,
rall.
p a tempo
Fl. & Cl.
pizz.
BESSIE.
jol-ly, lit-tle Love! Sor-row fol-lows fol-ly, As the ber-ries grow on hol-ly, And
oh! 'tis fol-ly, oh! 'tis fol-ly! And oh! 'tis fol-ly, To be a-fraid of
rit.

a tempo
B
BESSIE.
Love! With a hey, jol-ly, jol-ly, hey jol-ly, lit-tle Love!
JILL.
With a hey, jol-ly, jol-ly, hey jol-ly, lit-tle Love!
RALEIGH.
With a hey, oh!
ESSEX.
With a hey, jol-ly lit-tle Love!
LONG TOM.
With a hey, jol-ly lit-tle Love!
a tempo
pizz.
W. W.
B.
Sor-row fol-lows fol-ly, As the ber-ries grow on hol-ly, And Oh 'tis fol-ly,
J.
Sor-row fol-lows fol-ly, As the ber-ries grow on hol-ly, And Oh 'tis fol-ly,
R.
Sor-row fol-lows fol-ly, As the ber-ries grow on hol-ly, And Oh 'tis fol-ly,
ES.
Sor-row fol-lows fol-ly, As the ber-ries grow on hol-ly, And Oh 'tis fol-ly,
L.T.
Sor-row fol-lows fol-ly, As the ber-ries grow on hol-ly, And Oh 'tis fol-ly,

rit.
B.
Oh! 'tis fol - ly! And Oh! 'tis fol - ly, To be a fraid of
J.
Oh! 'tis fol - ly! And Oh! 'tis fol - ly, To be a - fraid of
R.
Oh! 'tis fol - ly! And Oh! 'tis fol - ly, To be a - fraid of
ES.
fol - ly, fol - ly! Oh! 'tis fol - ly, To be a - fraid of
L.T.
fol - ly, fol - ly! Oh! 'tis fol - ly, To be a - fraid of
rit.
C ENCORE
a tempo
Love!
Love!
Love!
Love!
Love!
p
a tempo

B. Love is but a but - ter - fly Hey! jol - ly, jol - ly hey,
J. Love is but a but - ter - fly Hey! ho!
R. Love is but a but - ter - fly Hey! jol - ly, jol - ly hey,
ES. Love is but a but - ter - fly Hey! ho!
L.T. Love is but a but - ter - fly Hey! ho!
Fl.
pizz.
B. What is there to match it? Will you watch it flut - ter by? Oh! fol - ly fol - ly, oh,
J. Hey ho! Will you watch it flut - ter by? Hey! ho!
R. What is there to match it? Will you watch it flut - ter by? Oh! fol - ly fol - ly, oh,
ES. Hey ho! Will you watch it flut - ter by? Hey! ho!
L.T. Hey ho! Will you watch it flut - ter by? Hey! ho!

B.
fol-ly not to catch it!
mf
Try to keep it when you've caught it!
J.
Hey! ho!
mf
Try to keep it when you've caught it!
R.
fol-ly not to catch it!
ES.
Hey! ho!
mf
Try to keep it when you've caught it!
L.T.
Hey! ho!
mf
Try to keep it when you've caught it!
Ob.
mf
Horn
B.
Ah!
Where-fore weep. Where-fore weep: Oh
p
J.
Ah!
Where-fore weep: Where-fore weep: Oh
p
R.
f
Where-fore weep: If you have sought it, Where-fore weep: Where-fore weep: Oh
mf
p
ES.
f
Where-fore weep: If you have sought it, Where-fore weep: Where-fore weep: Oh
mf
p
L.T.
Where-fore weep: If you have sought it, Where-fore weep: Where-fore weep: Oh
p

A (2nd Verse.)
animato
B.
Love is meant to make us glad,- is meant to make us glad!
J.
Love is meant to make us glad,- to make us glad!
R.
Love is meant to make us glad,- to make us glad!
ES.
Love is meant to make us glad,- is meant to make us glad!
L.T.
Love is meant to make us glad,- to make us glad!
W. W.
animato
Timp.
To sigh for it, and die for it, Oh, wis-dom ne-ver
To sigh for it, and die for it, Oh, wis-dom ne-ver
To sigh for it, and die for it, Oh, wis-dom ne-ver
To sigh for it, and die for
To sigh for it, and die for
f
pp

B.
taught it! With a hey jol-ly jol-ly hey,
J.
mf
taught it! Oh, wis-dom ne-ver taught it!
R.
taught it! With a hey jol-ly jol-ly hey,
ES.
it-
L.T.
mf
it- Oh, wis-dom ne-ver taught it!
B.
f
p a tempo
jol-ly lit-tle Love! Hey! lit-tle Love, With a hey!
J.
f
p
Hey! With a hey!
R.
f
p
jol-ly lit-tle Love! Hey! lit-tle Love, With a hey! jolly, jol-ly, hey,
ES.
f
p
Hey! With a hey!
L.T.
f
p
Hey! With a hey!
Fl. & Cl.
p
pizz.
f
rall.
a tempo
pp
Ped.
Ped.

B.
J.
R.
jol-ly lit-tle Love! Sor-row fol-lows fol-ly, As the ber-ries grow on hol-ly, And
ES.
L.T.
B.
J.
R.
rit.
oh, 'tis fol-ly, oh, 'tis fol-ly And oh, 'tis fol-ly To— run a-way from
ES.
L.T.
rit.

a tempo
B (2nd Verse.)
f
B.
With a hey, jol-ly jol-ly hey, jol-ly lit-tle Love!
J.
With a hey, jo jol-ly hey, jol-ly lit-tle Love!
R.
Love! With a hey, ho!
ES.
With a hey, jol - ly lit - tle Love!
L.T.
With a hey, jol - ly lit - tle Love!
a tempo
pizz.
mf
W. W.
ppp
Sorrow follows fol-ly, as the ber-ries grow on hol-ly, And oh, 'tis fol-ly
p

Broader.
rall.
pp
B.
Oh, 'tis fol - ly, And Oh, 'tis fol - ly, To— run a - way from
J.
Oh, 'tis fol - ly, And Oh, 'tis fol - ly, To run a - way from
R.
Oh, 'tis fol - ly, And Oh, 'tis fol - ly, To run a - way from
ES.
Oh, 'tis fol - ly, Oh, 'tis fol - ly, To run a - way from
L.T.
Oh, 'tis fol ly, Oh, 'tis fol - ly, To run a - way from
Broader.
rall.
C
(2nd Verse)
a tempo
accel.
f
Love! 'Tis fol - ly To— run a - way from Love!
Love! a - way from Love!
Love! a - way from Love!
Love! a - way from Love!
Love! a - way from Love!
a tempo
pp delicato

rall.
D
a tempo
E
pp
Picc.
Str.
Picc.
Str.
pizz.
pp

Nº 5. BALLAD.- (Bessie.)

"SHE HAD A LETTER FROM HER LOVE."

(BAND PARTS in B Minor.)

Allegretto semplice. ♩= 112.
pizz. & Fl.
Cl.
mf
p
Ped.
BESSIE.
She had a let - ter from her love And on her heart she
lost the let - ter from her love Or some - bo - dy did
pp arco (sus.)
A
laid it! 'Twas all in rhyme and Fa - ther Time She vow'd could ne - ver
steal it! And oh! the smart in her poor heart, She vow'd that nought could
pp
fade it. Ah! Ah
heal it. Ah! Ah
pp
Ob. & Cl.

rit.
me! Ah me! A lov_er's vow; She knoweth bet_ter
me! Ah me! A lov_er's vow; She knoweth bet_ter
mf
rit.
pp
ENCORE
1.
now. She
now.
B
a tempo
Cl.
mf
p
2.
f
She found the let_ter from her love When she had sore_ly
animato
f
Fag. & Horn.
p
miss'd it; Des_pite the stain of mud and rain She fond_led it, and
p

C
meno mosso.
kiss'd it. Ah! Ah
meno mosso.
rit.
me! Ah me! a lov-er's vow! She know-eth
Cl.
D
bet-ter now, Ah!
W. W. & Hrn.
accel.
rall.
rall.
She know-eth bet-ter now.
Str.
colla voce
Not

Nº 6. SONG.- (Essex) and CHORUS.

"THE YEOMEN OF ENGLAND."

Allegro marziale. ♩ = 138.
Tutti
f
S. Drum Solo
ESSEX.
Who were the Yeo-men- the Yeo-men of Eng-land?
Str.
f
S.D.
Brass.
Horns (sus.)
animato
The freemen were the Yeomen, the freemen of Eng-land! Stout were the
Cl.
Str.
p
sempre staccato
bows they bore, When they went out to war,- Stout-er their courage for the

A
ho-nour of Eng-land, And
S.D.
mf
sf
Brass
Na-tions to East-ward, And Na-tions to West-ward, As foe-men did curse them, The
pp
Str. & Brass stacc.
Bow-men of Eng-land! No o-ther land could nurse them, But their Mother-land, old
W. W.
allargando
Eng-land! And on her broad bo-som did they e-ver thrive!
Brass
allargando
f
S.D.

B
CHORUS.
CHORUS.
And Nations to East-ward, And Nations to
And Nations to East-ward, And Nations to
Tutti
simile
West-ward, As foe-men did curse them, The Bow-men of Eng-land! No
West-ward, As foe-men did curse them, The Bow-men of Eng-land! No
ten.
ESSEX and CHORUS unis.
o-ther land could nurse them, But their Mother-land Old Eng-land! And
o-ther land could nurse them, But their Mother-land Old Eng-land! And

ENCORE.
on her broad bo-som did they e - ver thrive!
animato
Str
mf
C ESSEX.
Where are the Yeo-men the
Trumpets
f
S. D. roll
Meno mosso.
Yeo-men of Eng-land?
In homestead and in
Str.
S.D. Brass
Str.
p
Animato.
Cottage They still dwell in Eng-land! Stained with the rud-dy tan,
sempre staccato

God's air doth give a man, Free as the winds that fan The broad breast of
Eng-land! And Na-tions to
D
S.D.
mf
Brass
sf
pp
Str. & Brass stacc.
East-ward, And Na - tions to West-ward, As foe-men may curse them, The
Yeo - men of Eng-land! No o-ther land can nurse them, But their Mother-land, old
W.W.

allargando
accel.
Eng-land! And on her broad bo-som Shall they e - ver thrive, shall
allargando
accel.
Brass
rall.
E
they, - shall they e - ver thrive!
CHORUS.
ff
And Na - tions to
ff
And Na - tions to
Tutti
rall.
f
a tempo
ff
ff
simile
CHORUS.
East-ward, And Na - tions to West-ward, As foe-men may curse them, The
East-ward, And Na - tions to West-ward, As foe-men may curse them, The

CHORUS.
ten.
Yeo-men of England! No o-ther land can nurse them, But their Mother-land, old
ten.
Yeo-men of England! No o-ther land can nurse them, But their Mother-land, old
ten.
ESSEX with CHORUS.
CHORUS.
ff
rall.
Eng-land! And on her broad bo-som Shall they e-ver
ff
rall.
Eng-land! And on her broad bo-som Shall they e-ver
ff
rall.
CHORUS.
ff
molto rall.
thrive, Shall they e - ver thrive!
ff
molto rall.
thrive, Shall they e - ver thrive!
Largamente.
Tpts.
ff
molto rall.
sff
sff
sff
sff

No. 7. DUET.—(Bessie and Raleigh.)

"COME TO ARCADIE."

Allegro con brio. ♩= 104.
Str. & W. W.
mf
RALEIGH.
leggiero
When true love hath found a man, He will hear the Pipe of Pan,
p
pp
Horn (sus.)
Fl.
R.
Pan, the god of o_pen coun_try, Oh, his tunes are
A Ob.
R.
pret_ty! Na_ture bids you bring your sweet one, Where no o_ther
Cl.

R.
soul may meet one. Ah! "Nature made the coun-try side,
mf
R.
And man did make the ci-ty."
(Beat 4)
arco
pp
rall. molto
pizz.
Ped.
B
(Beat 2)
meno mosso
accel.
Tempo I
R.
Come, come to Ar-ca-die! Bring your Phyl-lis, hap-py Co-ry-don!
pp meno mosso
accel.
Tempo I
R.
Learn to-ge-ther, if you can, The sim-ple tunes of Pi - per

(Beat 4)
(Beat 2)
BESSIE.
rall.
f allargando
accel.
mf a tempo
Ah! Come, come to Ar-ca-die, Bring your Phyl-lis
RALEIGH.
Pan! Come, come to Ar-ca-die, Bring your Phyl-lis
Fl. & Cl.
hap-py Co-ry-don! Ah! Learn to-ge-ther
hap-py Co-ry-don! Learn to-ge-ther, if you can, the tunes of
cresc.
if you can, Tra la, la, la, la, la, la, Come
Pi-per Pan! Come
pizz.
arco
Brass

ENCORE.
rit.
a tempo
B.
— to Ar - ca - die!
rit.
a tempo
R.
— to Ar - ca - die!
rit.
p a tempo
C BESSIE.
leggiero
When a maid doth love a man, She will hear the Pipe of Pan, —
p
B.
Pan will call her, call her, call her, —
Fl.
pp
Ob.
— With a mag - ic dit - ty! Bet - ter far a coun - try cot - tage
Cl.

B.
If your true love share your pot-tage Ah!
mf
B.
Than to dwell in Cas-tle Pride As some do, more's the
p
pizz.
D
Meno mosso. accel.
Tempo I.
B.
pi-ty!
(Beat 4)
Come, come to Ar-ca-die! I'll be Phyllis,
(Beat 2)
arco
rall. molto
pp
Ped.
*
B.
You be Co-ry-don! Hap-py maid and hap-py man, To dance all day for

(Beat 4)
BESSIE.
rall.
f allargando
accel.
Pi - per Pan! Come come to Ar - ca - die!
RALEIGH.
Ah! Come come to Ar - ca - die!
Fl. & Cl.
(Beat 2)
Tempo Iº
mf
I'll be Phyl-lis, You'll be Co-ry-don. Ah!
You'll be Phyl-lis, I'll be Co-ry-don. Learn to-ge-ther, if you can,
Hap-py maid and hap-py man, Tra la, la, la, la, la,
The tunes of Pi-per Pan,
cresc.
Ped. *
Brass

E
animato
B.
la, Come — to Ar-ça-die!
R.
Come — to Ar-ca-die! Come — to Ar-ca-die! Hap-py
pizz.
animato
p
arco
W.W. & Hrn.
Fl.
Tra la, la, la, la, la, Tra la, la, la, la, la,
maid and man, Come — to Ar - ca -
B.
la, Tra la, la, la, la, la, la, la, la, la, la, la, Tra la, la, la, la, la,
R.
- die! Hap - py maid and man, Come, —

Cl.
la, la, la, la, la, Tra la, la, la, la, la, la, la, la, la,
to Ar - ca - -
la, Tra la, la, la, la, la, la, la, la, la, la, la, la, la, la, la, la,
- die! Hap - py maid and man,
F
rit.
la, Come to Ar - ca - die!
Come to Ar - ca - die!
mf
rit.
p
Brass p

No. 8. ENTRANCE of QUEEN ELIZABETH.

Allegro alla Marcia. ♩= 116.
Tutti
mf
cresc. - - - molto - - -
C
ff
CHORUS.
Long live E - liz - a-beth! Sing with u - ni - ted breath,
Long live E - liz - a-beth! Sing with u - ni - ted breath,
ff
-beth ___ And Mer-rie Eng - land.
God save E - liz - a-beth, And Eng-land, Mer-rie Eng - land.
God save E - liz - a-beth, And Eng-land, Mer-rie Eng - land.

CHORUS.
May hea-ven pros-per her, May hea-ven fos-ter her. Saint
May_ hea-ven pros - per her, May hea - ven fos - ter her. Saint
Eng - land,___ And Eng. - land's Queen Bess.
CHORUS.
George for mer-rie Eng - land, And Eng - land's Queen Bess Queen
George for mer-rie Eng - land, And Eng - land's Queen Bess Queen
Tpts.
CHORUS.
Bess, Queen Bess!___ May
Bess, Queen Bess!___ May
p

D
CHORUS.
Hea - ven pros - per her, May Hea - ven fos - ter her, Saint
Hea - ven pros - per her, May Hea - ven fos - ter her, Saint
p
W. W. & Horns.
CHORUS.
George for mer - rie Eng - land And Eng - land's Queen
George for mer - rie Eng - land And Eng - land's Queen
CHORUS.
Bess, And Eng - land's Queen Bess! May Hea - ven pros - per her, May hea - ven
Bess, And Eng - land's Queen Bess! May Hea - ven pros - per her, May hea - ven
Ped. * Ped. *
Triang.

CHORUS.
fos - ter her. Saint George for mer - rie Eng - land and
fos - ter her. Saint George for mer - rie Eng - land and
CHORUS.
E
f
England's Queen! May Heav'n, may Hea - ven pros - per her. Long live E -
England's Queen! May Heav'n, may Hea - ven pros - per her.
mf
Brass
CHORUS.
- liz - a - beth, E - liz - - a - beth
f
Long live E -
f

CHORUS.
-liz - a-beth, Long live E -
CHORUS.
F Maestoso.
ff
Long live E - liz-a-beth! Loy - al and
rall.
ff
- liz - a-beth! Long live E - liz-a-beth! Loy - al and
rit.
Maestoso.
ff
Tutti
CHORUS.
true till death, un-to her English Queen shall Eng-land be.
true till death, un-to her English Queen shall Eng-land be.
3

CHORUS.
Held high, thy scep-tre is O - ver thine en-e-mies E -
Held high, thy scep - tre is O - ver thine en - e-mies E -
Eng-land, And
G
animato
cresc.
CHORUS.
- liz - a-beth for Eng - land, And Eng - land for thee E -
- liz - a - beth for Eng - land, And Eng - land, Eng - land for
Più vivo.
cresc.
Ped.
*
CHORUS.
- liz - a-beth for Eng - land, and Eng - land, and Eng - -
thee. E - liz - a-beth for Eng - land, and Eng - -
mf

CHORUS.
ff
- land for thee!
ff
- land for thee!
WAit
Wait!
ff
SIT
accel.
molto
H Tempo di Minuetto. (Not too fast.)
Cl.
p
sf sf
ten.
Horns
pizz.
Fl.
tr
rall.
Segue

No 9. SONG (Elizabeth.) with CHORUS.

(Chorus sit during this number.)

Moderato. (Not too fast.)
ELIZABETH.
tranquillo
O peace-ful England,
Str. & Cl.
♩= 92.
tranquillo
p
pp
Horn (sus.)
While I my watch am keep-ing, Thou, like Mi-ner-va
Wea-ry of war, art sleep-ing.
CHORUS.
pp
Wea-ry of war, art sleep-ing.
pp
Wea-ry of war, art sleep-ing.
pp
W.W.

ELIZABETH.
Sleep on a lit-tle while, And in thy slum-ber smile.
mp
While thou art sleep-ing I'll Be wake - ful, e-ver wake - ful
f
f
rit.
K a tempo
p
Ah! Sword and
dim.
pp
buck-ler by thy side, Rest on the shore of bat-tle-tide, Which, like the

p
e-ver hun-gry sea,_ Howls round this_ Isle. O
L
sleep till I a-wa-ken thee, And in thy slum-ber smile!
Str.
W. W.
pp
mf
ENCORE.
p
tranquillo
Eng-land, fair Eng-land, Well hast thou earned thy slum-ber,
tranquillo
pp

Yet though thy bo-som No breast-plate now en-cum-ber.
J (2nd Verse)
pp
CHORUS.
ELIZABETH.
f animato
No breast-plate now en-cum-ber. Let not thy fingers yield
pp
No breast-plate now en-cum-ber.
animato
pp
mf
W.W.
Grasp of thy sword and shield. Thou shalt a-
Largamente
ff
-wake and wield Des-truc-tion, when I call thee!
ff

K (2nd Verse)
p
Ah
Sword and
accel.
dim.
rit.
pp
buck-ler by thy side, Rest on the shore of bat-tle-tide Which, like the
p
e-ver hun-gry sea, Howls round this Isle. O
L (2nd Verse)
sleep till I a-wa-ken thee, And in thy slum-ber smile!
Fl.
pp

pp
Sword and buckler by thy side, Rest on the shore of bat-tle-tide Which, like the
pp
Sword and buckler by thy side, Rest on the shore of bat-tle-tide Which, like the
pp
tranquillo
pp
dim.
ever hungry sea, Howls round this Isle! O sleep till she a-wakens thee, And
pp
dim.
ever hungry sea, Howls round this Isle! O sleep till she a-wakens thee, And
pp
dim.
ELIZ.
pp
rit.
ppp
And in thy slum-ber, smile!
pp
ppp
in thy slum-ber smile! And in thy slum-ber, smile!
pp
ppp
in thy slum-ber smile! And in thy slum-ber, smile!
Str. & W.W.
mf
pp
rit
ppp
Voices only

No 10. FINALE-ACT I.

Allegro giocoso. ♩= 116.
Str. & W.W.
f
p
Tamp.
BESSIE.
con anima.
It is a tale of Rob - in Hood, of
Str.
pp con anima.
Ped.
B.
Tuck, and lit - tle John, And all of those who fol-lowed him With
rall.
a tempo
Ped.
B.
his Maid Ma-ri - on, With his Maid Ma - ri - on. For she,
Ob.
Ped.

B.
for she fol-lowed him, As
Fl.
Tamb.
A
f
Love may fol-low thee. Be-neath the green-wood
f
p
tree. Tho for-tune frown, Thou'lt wear a crown A King may nev-er
see!
CHORUS.
f
As Love may fol-low thee, Be-neath the green-wood tree Tho'
f
As Love may fol-low, fol-low thee, Be
f
Tutti

Fl.
BESSIE.
B
p
With a hey, Rob-in,
CHORUS
for-tune frown Thoult wear a crown A king may nev-er see!
-neath the green-wood, green-wood tree!
pizz.
p delicato.
B.
rall.
jol-ly, jol-ly Rob-in, Hey, Rob-in, jol-ly, jol-ly Rob-in, What tho' for-tune
rall.
Horn (sus.)
B.
a tempo.
wear a frown, With a hey, jol-ly, jol-ly, Rob-in!
CHORUS.
f
Hey,
With a hey, jol-ly, jol-ly Rob-in, Hey,
With a hey, jol-ly, jol-ly Rob-in, jol-ly, jol-ly
f
With a hey, jol-ly hey, jol-ly
f a tempo.

Rob-in jol-ly
sf
Rob-in jol-ly, jol-ly Rob-in hey! ho, hey ho!
Rob-in jol-ly Rob-in hey! ho, hey ho!
CHORUS.
hey, jol-ly, jol-ly Rob-in hey! ho!
f
Tamb.
BESSIE.
Then
Cl.
p
C
B.
who would not be out of court As Rob-in Hood be-fel? To fare as love may
Str.
Ped. * Ped. *
rall. a tempo.
B.
bid him fare! And bid all else fare-well, And bid all else fare-
rall a tempo.

accel.
B.
-well. If love fol-low him, If love fol-low fol-low fol-low
Fl. & Cl.
p
accel.
f
him, If love fol - low
Cl. Solo
f
p colla voce
a tempo
him As
p
If love fol - low
CHORUS.
p
If love fol - low
a tempo
Fl.
W.W.
L.H.
p

D
B.
love may fol - low thee Be - neath the green-wood
CHORUS.
him
him
f
p
B.
tree, Tho' for - tune frown Thou'lt wear a crown A King may nev - er
B.
see!
CHORUS.
f
As love may fol - low thee, Beneath the green-wood tree! Tho'
As love may fol - low, fol - low thee, Be -
Tutti

F1.

BESSIE.
B.
With a Hey, Ro-bin
CHORUS.
for - tune frown, Thoul't wear a crown A King may nev-er see!
-neath the green - wood green - wood tree!
p delicato.
jol-ly jol-ly jol-ly Ro-bin Hey, Ro-bin, jol-ly jol-ly Ro-bin, What tho' for - tune
rall.
wear a frown, With a hey, jol-ly, jol-ly Ro-bin,
a tempo.
f
With a hey, jol - ly, jol - ly Ro-bin, Hey,
jol-ly, jol-ly
With a hey, jol - ly Ro - bin, A
a tempo

E animato.
B.
Ro-bin jol-ly Ro-bin, With a hey, jol-ly Ro-bin,
CHORUS.
animato.
Ro-bin jol-ly jol-ly Ro-bin, With a hey, jol-ly Ro-bin,
Ro-bin jol-ly Ro-bin,
animato.
hey, jol-ly, jol-ly Ro-bin, With a hey, jol-ly Ro-bin,
W.W.
B.
jol-ly Ro-bin.
CHORUS.
jol-ly Ro-bin.
ff unis.
jol-ly Ro-bin. With a hey, Ro-bin,
ff
Ped. *
Brass
CHORUS.
ff unis.
With a hey, Ro-bin, jol-ly, jol-ly Ro-bin hey! ho!
jol-ly, jol-ly Ro-bin, hey, Ro-bin, jol-ly Ro-bin, hey! ho!
Picc.

CHORUS.
hey ho!
hey ho!
Fl. & Cl.
dim.
sempre.
F
RECIT.
ELIZABETH.
Would Queens could love as
rit.
RECIT.
pp
p
a tempo
EL.
Mar-ion did! Heigh-ho! heigh-ho!
ESSEX.
Would I ______ were Ro-bin
Vio. I°
a tempo
f
Ped.
Cello
LONG TOM. (Sung by Essex)
E.
Hood if that were so (Heigh-ho! heigh-ho!)
Ma-dam, I ask a
Ob.
p
Horn

G
L.T.
fa - vour!
Tutti
I plead the
Animato.
sf
dim.
p
Str.
con espress.
cause of a poor, sore-ly strick-en girl, Whom
folk do call "Jill - all - a - lone."
SOPRANO CHORUS.
She is a
Allegro vivace.
fff
Brass.
CHORUS.
witch! She is a witch! She is a witch! She is a
(CONT.)
She is a witch! She is a
unis.
a witch!
sf

unis
rall.
CHORUS.
witch! She is a witch! a witch, a witch, a witch!
She is a witch! She is a witch! a witch, a witch, a witch!
8
sf
rall.
H a tempo
Oh, she's a witch! Pick up a stone! Die in a ditch!
Oh, she's a witch! Pick up a stone! Die in a ditch!
ff a tempo
Tutti
ff largamente
a tempo.
Jill - all - a - lone!
ff
Jill - all - a - lone!
largamente
ff
a tempo.
Cymbal (with stick)

CHORUS.
Str.
J
RECIT.
ELIZABETH
Who speak a-gainst her?
Horn
p
Moderato.
mf a tempo
Fag.
Timp. Solo
CONTRALTO CHORUS.
These four worthy
Fl. & Ob.
tr
sf sf
Allegro. ♩.= 138.
K
CON.
cit-izens of Wind-sor town!
p
f

TAILOR.
We're four men of Wind-sor, We're four - men of
BAKER.
We're four men of Wind-sor, We're four - men of
TINKER.
We're four men of Wind-sor, We're four - men of
BUTCHER.
We're four men of Wind-sor, We're four - men of
f
Cello (sus.)
T.
Wind - sor,
B.
Wind - sor, A Ba-ker of Windsor,
TI.
Wind - sor, A
BA.
Wind - sor, A But-cher of Wind-sor,
Str.
p
sempre staccato.

T.
B.
TI.
BA.
A Tai-lor of Windsor,
And good bread I bake!
Tin-ker of Windsor,
And
And good meat I sell!
Fl.
And good clothes I make! So we all ply a good trade in
So we all ply a good trade in
my tin is good tin! So we all ply a good trade in
So we all ply a good trade in

T.
Wind-sor town And cry Who'll buy?
B.
Wind-sor town And cry Who'll buy?
TI.
Wind-sor town Who'll buy? Who'll
BA.
Wind-sor town Who'll buy? Who'll
Ob. & Cl.
Fl.
L
T.
Who'll buy? buy? buy? buy? From the four men of
B.
Who'll buy? buy? buy? buy? From the four men of
TI.
buy? Who'll buy? buy? buy? buy? buy? From the four men of
BA.
buy? Who'll buy? buy? buy? buy? buy? From the four men of
f

TAI.
Wind-sor town, From the four men of Wind - sor.
BA.
Wind-sor town, From the four men of Wind - sor.
TI.
Wind-sor town, From the four men of Wind - sor.
BU.
Wind-sor town, From the four men of Wind - sor.
LL
BUTCHER.
LU.
When you buy meat, try my meat.
Cl.
pp
delicato
Horn (stopped)
BAKER.
BA
When you buy bread, try my bread.
TINKER.
When you
Ob.
Fag.

TAILOR.
TI.
buy tin, try my tin. When you buy clothes, try
Fl.
Picc.
my clothes.
CHORUS.
f
From the four men of Wind-sor
f
From the four men of Wind-sor
Trumpet
f
Brass
CHORUS.
town, From the four men of Wind - sor, The four men of Windsor all
mf
town, From the four men of Wind - sor, The four men of Windsor all
W.W.
p

TA.
BA.
TI.
BU.
The
CHORUS.
ply a good trade, O the four men of Windsor all ply a good trade. O the
The
The
The Bak-er of Wind-sor,
The Tin-ker of Wind-sor,
Butch-er of Wind-sor,
Butch - er, Bak - - er, Tin - - ker,
Butch - er, Bak - - er, Tin - - ker,
Str.
sempre staccato
Triang.

Tai - lor of Windsor Butch - er, Bak - er,
BA.
Butch - er, Bak - er,
TL.
Butch - er, Bak - er,
Butch - er, Bak - er,
CHORUS.
Tai - - lor The Butch-er of Wind-sor, The Bak-er of Windsor, The
Tai - - lor The Bak-er of Windsor,
TA.
Tin - - ker, Tai - - lor,
BA.
Tin - - ker, Tai - - lor, And
TL.
Tin - - ker, Tai - - lor,
BU.
Tin - - ker, Tai - - lor, And good meat I sell!
CHORUS.
And all
Tin-ker of Windsor, The Tai-lor of Wind-sor, And Butch - er
The Tai-lor of Wind-sor, And Butch - er

TA.
And good clothes I make! And we
BA.
good bread I bake!
And we
TI.
And my tin is good tin!
And we
BU.
And we
ply a good trade
CHORUS.
Bak - er, Tin - ker, Tai - lor And
Bak - er, Tin - ker, Tai - lor And
TA.
all ply a good trade in Wind - sor town. And cry
A.
all ply a good trade in Wind - sor town. And cry
TI.
all ply a good trade in Wind - sor town. Who'll
BU.
all ply a good trade in Wind - sor town. Who'll
CHORUS.
all ply a good trade in Wind - sor town.
all ply a good trade in Wind - sor town.
f

TA.
Who'll buy? Who'll buy? buy?
BA.
Who'll buy? Who'll buy? buy?
TI.
buy? Who'll buy? Who'll buy? buy? buy?
BU.
buy? Who'll buy? Who'll buy? buy? buy?
CHORUS.
Mf
TA.
buy? buy? From the four men of Wind - sor town, From the
BA.
buy? buy? From the four men of Wind - sor town, From the
TI.
buy? buy? From the four men of Wind - sor town, From the
BU.
buy? buy? From the four men of Wind - sor town, From the
CHORUS.
From the four men of Wind - sor town, From the
From the four men of Wind - sor town, From the
Ped. *
Brass

Presto.
A.
four men of Wind - sor town.
A.
four men of Wind - sor town.
T.
four men of Wind - sor town.
BU.
four men of Wind - sor town.
CHORUS.
four men of Wind - sor town.
four men of Wind - sor town.
Str.
Presto.
f
accel.

RECIT.
N
ELIZABETH:
a tempo
What say you girl? They say you are a witch!
Tutti
Allegro molto.
Cl.
RECIT.
sf
a tempo
ff
Cymb.
JILL. Recit.
A witch is wise, So
Horn
pp
Moderato.
if a witch I do know more than they_ But if I am a witch I know much
ppp
Str.
Fl.
ppp
ad lib.
less, Be-cause I do not know I am a witch; But I do know what I do know!
W.W. (sus.)
cresc.

a tempo
Allegretto con tenerezza. (Not too Slow.)
J.
Now hark! I know that love is
Str.
f a tempo
p
pp
Ped.
far a-bove all o-ther pret-ty things, And I do know That
Ped.
be-ing so, 'Tis co-vet-ed by kings. But love hath
wings, And pass-eth by A King, some-times, For such as

J.
pp
I. I won-der why! I won-der why!
Ob.
pp
pp
Ped. Tri. *
O Allegro agitato.
SOPRANO CHORUS.
a tempo
f
By those words we ac-cuse her Of draw-ing by her mag-ic, The
sfp
sf
Brass
Str.
SOP.
3
love of faith-ful lov-ers Un-to her - self; By witch-craft, by
sfp
sfp
sfp
SOP.
which-craft! by witch - craft!
ESSEX.
She had this piece of
sfp
sfp
f
p
Timp.

ES.
writ-ing Which I did find up - on her.
per-
W.W.
-haps_ it is a love charm,
A thing of e-vil pur-pose!
pizz.
arco
ES.
Q
Allargando..
dim.
ELIZABETH.
The verse is an a-cros-tic, And its in-i-tial let-ters Do make the name of

Allegro gicoso.
(with great animation.)
EL.
"Bes-sie!"
Fl. & pizz.
And I do know the writ-ing!
pp
f p
ppp
ESSEX.
'Tis Sir Wal-ter Ra-leigh's.
ELIZABETH.
Yes! Yes!
(to Raleigh.)
EL.
Is it not thy writ-ing, and my name that is writ-ten?
RALEIGH.
R.
The writ-ing is my writ-ing, And I give back the let-ter To
Str.
sf pp

Agitato.
R.
her, to her for whom I wrote it.
CHORUS.
Bes-sie Throck-
Bes-sie Throck-
Allegro molto.
colla voce
Brass
rall.
molto
-mor - ton! Bes-sie Throck-mor - - ton!
-mor - ton! Bes-sie Throck-mor - - ton!
rall.
Timp.
R Allegro moderato.
con moto.
R.
My troth is plight-ed To this gen - - tle maid
Allegro moderato.
con moto.
Str.

R.
In se - cret I have paid My past ad - dress - es!
Cl.
Blow high, blow low, How - ev - er for - tune blow, I
rall.
let the whole world know My heart is
BESSIE.
a tempo
Tho' I'm af-frighted And
Bes-sie's! My heart, my heart is Bes-sie's!
pp
pp

B.
sore a-fraid, Though dread of her ti-rade My
R.
My troth is plight - - ed to this
B.
soul pos-sess - es! Blow high, blow low, How
R.
maid; In se-cret I have paid my past ad- -
B.
ev-er for-tune blow I'll let the whole world go For thy ca-
R.
-dress - - es, I let, I let the whole world
f

ELIZABETH.
p
f animato
B.
-ress-es, For thy for thy ca-ress-es! Now I am slighted For an-
R.
p
know my heart, my heart is Bes-sie's!
pp
p animato
ten.
Timp.
Fl.
EL.
-oth - er maid, Love's like a fal - con strayed, With
EL.
bro - ken jess-es! Fly high, fly low, Wher - ev - er love may go,
EL.
What lure can wo - man throw For lost ca - ress - es!
Brass
GET READY OVER

Grandioso.
BESSIE.
molto rall.
ff
Ah! Tho' I'm af-fright-ed and
ELIZABETH.
Ah!
RALEIGH.
ff
Ah! My troth is plight-ed to this
ESSEX.
Grandioso.
S.
Ah! In love u-ni-ted They are
A.
f
ff
Ah! In love u-ni-ted
T.
f
ff
Ah! In love u-ni-ted
B.
f
ff
Ah In love u-ni-ted
Grandioso.
rall. molto
ff
Timp.
Tutti

B.
sore a - fraid, Tho' dread of her ti-rade my
EL.
Now I am slight - ed for an -
R.
gen - - - tle maid; In se - cret I have paid my
ES.
Now thou art slight - - - ed for an -
S.
not a - fraid, Tho' jeal - ous of her maid Our
A.
They are not a - fraid, Tho' jeal - ous
T.
They are not a - fraid, Tho' jeal - ous
B.
They are not a - fraid, Tho' jeal - ous

B.
soul pos-ses - es, Blow high, blow low, How
EL.
- oth - er maid. Love's like a fal - con
R.
past ad-dress - es. Blow high, blow low, How
ES.
- oth - er maid Love's like a fal - con strayed, with
S.
good Queen Bess is! Blow high, blow low, How
A.
of her maid Our good Queen Bess is! Blow
T.
of her maid Our good Queen Bess is! Blow
B.
of her maid Our good Queen Bess is! Blow

B.
- ev - er for-tune blow I let the whole world go For
EL.
strayed, with bro - ken jes - ses! What
RA.
- ev - er for-tune blow, I let the whole world know my
ES.
bro - ken jes - ses! what cure, what
S.
- ev - er for-tune blow, He'll let the whole world go For
A.
How -
high, blow low! How - ev - er for - tune
T.
high, blow low! How - ev - er for - tune
B.
high, blow low! How - ev - er for - tune

Largamente.
fff
dim. e molto rall.
B.
thy ca-ress-es, for thy, for thy ca-ress-es.
EL.
cure can wo - men know for lost, for lost ca-ress-es.
RA.
heart is Bessie's my heart my heart is Bessie's.
ES.
cure can wo - men know for lost, for lost ca-ress-es.
S.
her ca-ress-es, For her for her ca-ress-es.
A.
blow, He'll let the whole world go For her ca - ress-es.
T.
blow, He'll let the whole world go For her ca - ress-es.
B.
blow, He'll let the whole world go For her ca - ress-es.
Largamente.
Horns
dim. e molto rall.
mf

Allegretto.
JILL.
Not too Slow.
Ah! I know that love Is
mf
dim.
pp
W.W.
far a-bove All jew-els that are seen! And I do know That, be-ing so, 'Tis
J.
wan-ted by a Queen. But love, I ween, May pass her by. So
Horns
Agitato. ELIZABETH
I may laugh! so I may laugh! No! thou shalt die! Thou shalt
sf p
Str.

Allegro molto.
RECIT.
Agitato.
EL.
die!
Go! lodge this witch with-in the cas-tle walls! I'll see her
sf
sf pp
Allegro.
burn there!
Tutti
Str.
sf
ff
RECIT.
Allegro.
Thou, Sir Wal-ter, go to thy coun-try house and ban - ish-ment!
pp
f
Ob.
(To Bessie.)
rall. molto
Go to the cas-tle, thou a pris - o-ner! a pris - o-ner! a pris - o -
sf p
cresc. e
rall. molto
Brass

T Allegro appassionato.
ELIZ.
-ner
BESS.
Tho' I'm af-fright-ed and sore a-fraid,
RAL.
My troth is plight-ed to this gen-tle maid;
Fl.
Ob.
f Str.
Ped.
*
B.
Tho'dread of her ti-rade My soul po-ses-ses, Blow high, blow low, How-
R.
In se-cret I have paid My past ad-dress-es. Blow high, blow low, How-
p
B.
-ev-er for-tune blow, I'll let the whole world go For
R.
-ev-er for-tune blow, I let the whole world go For

B.
thy ca-res-ses, for thy for thy ca-res-ses!
R.
thy ca-res-ses, for thy, for thy caresses!
Entrance of MORRIS DANCERS.
Allegro.
CHORUS.
SOP. & TEN.
TUTTI.
Hey, hey, hey, hey, hey, hey, hey,
pizz.
S. Drum
Cho.
hey, Hey, hey, hey,
Fl. & Cl.
Cho.
Ah!
Ah!
arco

B.
p
If Love ___ do fol-low thee, Beneath the green-wood tree, Tho'
R.
p
If Love ___ do fol-low thee, Ah! ___ Tho'
ES.
p
If Love do follow thee, fol-low thee, Beneath the green-wood tree, Tho'
Beneath the green-wood tree, Tho'
S.
pp
Ah! ___
A.
pp
Ah! ___
T.
pp
Ah! ___
B.
pp
If Love do fol-low thee, fol-low thee, fol - low thee, fol-low
Fl. & Str.
pp

ff
B.
Fortune frown Thou'lt wear a crown a King may ne-ver see! If love
R.
For-tune frown Thou'lt wear a crown a King may ne-ver see!
ES.
For-tune frown Thou'lt wear a crown a King may ne-ver see!
For-tune frown Thou'lt wear a crown a King may ne-ver see!
unis.
S.
If Love do fol-low
A.
Ah! If Love do fol-low
T.
Ah! If Love do
B.
thee, fol-low thee, fol-low thee, fol-low thee, If Love do
f
B.D. & Cym. Tutti

B.
fol - low thee.
R.
ES.
S.
thee Be-neath the green-wood tree, Tho' For-tune frown, Thou'lt wear a crown a
A.
thee Be-neath the green-wood tree, Tho' For-tune frown, Thou'lt wear a crown a
T.
fol - low fol - low thee, Tho' For-tune frown Thou'lt wear a crown a
B.
fol - low fol - low thee, Be - neath the green - wood,

B.
R.
ES.
S.
A.
T.
B.
With a hey, Ro-bin jol-ly, jol-ly Ro-bin, hey, Ro-bin,
With a hey, Ro-bin jol-ly, jol-ly Ro-bin, hey,
With a hey, Ro-bin jol-ly, jol-ly Ro-bin, hey Ro-bin,
King may ne-ver see! With a hey, Ro-bin jol-ly, jol-ly Ro-bin, hey, Ro-bin
King may ne-ver see! With a hey, Ro-bin jol-ly, jol-ly Ro-bin, hey,
King may ne-ver see! With a hey, Ro-bin jol-ly, jol-ly Ro-bin, hey, Ro-bin,
green - wood tree! With a hey, Ro-bin jol-ly, jol-ly Ro-bin, hey, Ro-bin,

B.
jol-ly, jol-ly Ro-bin, What tho' for - tune wear a frown, With a hey!
R.
jol - ly Ro-bin, hey ho! hey ho! With a hey!
ES.
jol - ly Ro-bin, hey ho! hey ho! With a
S.
jol-ly, jol-ly Ro-bin, What tho' for - tune wear a frown, With a hey!
A.
jol - ly Ro-bin, What tho' for - tune wear a frown, With a hey!
T.
jol-ly, jol-ly Ro-bin, What tho' for - tune wear a frown, With a hey!
B.
jol - ly Ro-bin, What tho' for - tune wear a frown, With a
f

B.
— jol-ly, jol-ly Ro-bin hey, Ro-bin, jol - ly Ro-bin
R.
jol - ly, a hey jol-ly, jol-ly Ro-bin jol - ly Ro-bin
ES.
hey ho! With a hey ho! With a hey jol-ly, jol-ly Ro-bin!
S.
— jol-ly, jol-ly Ro-bin hey Ro-bin jol - ly Ro-bin! Tho'
A.
jol - ly, jol - ly Ro-bin, hey Ro-bin jol-ly, jol-ly Ro-bin! Tho'
T.
jol - ly, jol - ly Ro-bin, jol-ly, jol-ly Ro-bin jol - ly Ro-bin! Tho'
B.
hey! jol - ly Ro-bin, With a hey! jol-ly, jol-ly Ro-bin! Tho'

Molto Allegro.
B.
A King may ne
R.
A King may ne
E.
Tho' For-tune frown Thou'lt wear
CHORUS.
For-tune frown Thou'lt wear a crown a King, a King,
For-tune frown Thou'lt wear a crown a King, a King,
For-tune frown Thou'lt wear a crown a King, a King,
For-tune frown Thou'lt wear a crown a King, a King,
Molto Allegro.

rall. molto
B.
- - - ver, may ne-ver see. With a
R.
- - - ver, may ne-ver see. With a
E.
— a crown a King may ne-ver see. With a
CHORUS.
— A King may ne-ver see. Thou'lt wear —— a crown. With a
— A King may ne - ver see. Thou'lt wear —— a crown. With a
— A King may ne - ver see. Thou'lt wear —— a crown. With a
— A King may ne - ver see. Thou'lt wear —— a crown. With a
rall. molto

B.
fff a tempo
hey, Ro-bin, jol-ly, jol-ly Ro-bin, hey, Ro-bin jol-ly, jol-ly Ro-bin, Thou'lt wear a
R.
fff a tempo
hey, Ro-bin, jol-ly, jol-ly Ro-bin, hey, Ro-bin jol-ly, jol-ly Ro-bin, Thou'lt wear a
E.
fff a tempo
hey, Ro-bin, jol-ly, jol-ly Ro-bin, hey, Ro-bin jol-ly, jol-ly Ro-bin, Thou'lt wear a
fff a tempo
hey, Ro-bin, jol-ly, jol-ly Ro-bin, hey, Ro-bin jol-ly, jol-ly Ro-bin, Thou'lt wear a
fff a tempo
hey, Ro-bin, jol-ly, jol-ly Ro-bin, hey, Ro-bin jol-ly, jol-ly Ro-bin, Thou'lt wear a
fff a tempo
hey, Ro-bin, jol-ly, jol-ly Ro-bin, hey, Ro-bin jol-ly, jol-ly Ro-bin, Thou'lt wear a
fff a tempo
hey, Ro-bin, jol-ly, jol-ly Ro-bin, hey, Ro-bin jol-ly, jol-ly Ro-bin, Thou'lt wear a
fff a tempo
sf

B.
crown a King may ne-ver see!
R.
crown a King may ne-ver see!
E
crown a King may ne-ver see!
CHORUS.
crown a King may ne-ver see!
crown a King may ne-ver see!
crown a King may ne-ver see!
crown a King may ne-ver see!
animato
Ped. *
B.D. & Cym.
accel.
rall.
sf
ff
Timp. Solo

END OF ACT I.

Act II.

No 11. OPENING CHORUS with SOLO.—(Jill.)

Allegro. ♩.= 120.
Cello
Viola
Vio. 2
Vio. 1
f
Timp.
mf
Fag. & Hns.
Cl.
Ped.
A
sf
Horn.
Fl. & Picc.
p

Ped.
*
STAND
B
f
Tutti
Fl. & Picc.
C
sf
dim.
Stand
Str.
sempre
Brass

CHORUS.
mf
The month O' May has come to-day, And who will wear a
mf
The month O' May has come to-day, And who will wear a
p
Chorus alone.
CHORUS.
frown-a! The month O' May has come to-day, And who will wear a
frown-a! The month O' May has come to-day, And who will wear a
Ped.
D
Not too fast.
CHORUS.
frown-a! For where's the knave who'll not be mer-ry, We'll dig his grave with a
frown-a! For where's the knave who'll not be mer-ry, We'll dig his grave with a
Not too fast.

CHORUS.
der-ry down der-ry, We'll dig his grave with a der-ry down der-ry, A
der-ry down der-ry, We'll dig his grave with a der-ry down der-ry, A
CHORUS.
down, a down, a
down, a down, a der-ry down der-ry, a down, down, a derry down der-ry a
TENOR. Ah! Ah!
down, a down, a down, a down, a
CHORUS.
down, a der-ry down, down. Then where's the knave who'll
down, a der-ry down, der - ry down. Then where's the knave who'll

CHORUS.
not be mer-ry, We'll dig his grave with a der-ry down der-ry, a down
not be mer-ry, a down, a down, a down, a down, a down,
CHORUS.
a With a der-ry down der-ry, a der-ry down der-ry, a down
a With a down, a down, a down, a down, a down
E
CHORUS.
a.
a.
Orch.
Str.

F
Meno mosso.
mf JILL.
Str.
(Karp)
Cat, cat, where have you been?
Fl.
I've been to the Castle to look at the Queen!
Cat, cat, did she sit on a throne?
Ve-ri-ly, yes, like a
G
Jill all a-lone.
Cat, cat, what do you mean?
Ob.

J.
A Queen is a wo-man a wo-man a Queen.
f
Cat, cat, shall I sit on the throne?
Cl.
p
Ve-ri-ly, yes, When a
pp
H
lov-er you own, when a lov - er you own!
Not too fast
a tempo
Str. (sus.)
cresc.
Timp. & Tpts.
CHORUS.
mf
The Queen O' May is crown'd to day With a
Chorus alone.
f

crown, a crown, a crown-a, The Queen O' May is
crown, a crown, a crown-a, The Queen O' May is
Not too fast.
crown'd to-day With a crown, a crown, a crown-a. Then where's the knave who'll
crown'd to-day With a crown, a crown, a crown-a. Then where's the knave who'll
Not too fast.
not be mer-ry, And join the stave With a der-ry down der-ry, And
not be mer-ry, And join the stave With a der-ry down der-ry, And

join the stave With a der-ry down der-ry, a down, a down, a
Ah
join the stave With a der-ry down der-ry, a down, a
down, a down, a
der-ry down der-ry, A down, down, a der-ry down, der-ry a
Ah
down, a down, a down, a
down, A der-ry down, down. Then where's the knave who'll
sf
down, A der-ry down der - ry, down. Then where's the knave who'll
sf

ppp
not be mer-ry And join the stave With a der-ry down der-ry, a down
ppp
not be mer-ry A down, a down, a down, a down, a down
ppp
ff
a, With a der-ry down der-ry a der-ry down der-ry, a down
ff
a, With a down, a down, a down, a down, a down
ff
Ped. * Ped. *
a!
a!
Orch.
ff
pizz.
sf
sf
Ped. * Ped. Ped. * Ped.

No 12 QUARTET.

Allegro marcato. ♩ = 126.
BESSIE.
JILL.
In
RALEIGH.
In Eng-land, Mer-rie Eng-land, In
ESSEX.
In Eng-land, Mer-rie Eng-land, In
Allegro marcato. ♩ = 126.
Str. & Hrns.
B.
In Eng-land, Mer-rie Eng-land, Mer-rie
J.
Eng-land, Mer-rie Eng-land, In Eng-land, Mer-rie Eng-land, Mer-rie
R.
Eng-land, Mer-rie Eng-land, In Eng-land, Mer-rie Eng-land, Mer-rie
ES.
Eng-land, Mer-rie Eng-land, In Eng-land, Mer-rie Eng-land, Mer-rie

A
B.
J.
R.
ES.
Eng-land,
Eng-land,
Eng-land,
Eng-land,
There lived a king up - on a time To tell his name might
Str.
Fag. (sus.)
In Eng-land, Mer-rie Eng-land.
In Eng-land, Mer-rie Eng-land.
In Eng-land, Mer-rie Eng-land.
be a crime;
But he sometimes did doff his crown, And
Fl. & Ob.
Str.

B
B.
J.
RA.
ES.
In England, Merrie England, in
walk abroad like any clown.
W.W.
England, Merrie England.
And if he met a pretty wench, (And
Ob.

B.
J.
RA.
ES.
In__ Eng-land, Mer-rie Eng-land!
In__ Eng-land, Mer-rie Eng-land!
In__ Eng-land, Mer-rie Eng-land!
maids are fair-er than the French) In__ Eng-land, He'd
Fl.
Ob.
C ESSEX.
kiss her, as an Eng-lish-man Should kiss a mai-den, when he
colla voce
ENCORE.
So
So
So
animato
can!
So

D with great spirit
B.
let us sing, God save the King Of Eng-land, Mer-rie Eng-land!
J.
let us sing, God save the King Of Eng-land, Mer - rie Eng-land!
RA.
let us sing, God save the King Of Eng-land, Mer - rie Eng-land!
ES.
let us sing, God save the King Of Eng-land, Mer - rie Eng-land! With a
f pizz.
Cello
B.
With a fal la la
J.
With a fal la la la la la la la la la
RA.
With a fal la la la la la la la With a fal
ES.
fal la la la For Bluff King Hal, With a fal la la la la la la la la
Cl.
Fl.
Fag.

ppp
mf
B.
fal la la, With a fa la la la la la la la la la la la la la la la la
J.
la la la la la la la la la, la la la la la la la, la la la
RA.
la, With a fal la la la la la la la la la, With a fal la
ES.
la la la la la la la la la la la la la la la la la la la la
B.
la, la la la la la la la la la la la la, la la la la la, la la la la la la, la
J.
la la la la la la la la la la la la la la la la la la la la la la
RA.
la, With a fal la la la la la la la la la la la
ES.
la, al la la la la la la la la la, la la la la la, la la la la
Picc.&W.W.

E
B.
la la, With a fal la lal For Bluff King Hal; With a
J.
la la, With a fal la lal For Bluff King Hal; With a
RA.
la la, With a fal la lal For Bluff King Hal; With a
ES.
la la, With a fal la lal For Bluff King Hal; With a
Horn.
Fl.
B.
fal la la la la la la la la la la la fal la la la la la
J.
fal la la la la la la la la fal la
RA.
fal la la la la la la la la fal la
ES.
fal la la la la la la la la fal la
Str.

MEN STAND
rall.
pp a tempo
ff
B.
la la la la la la la la la la la la la, With a
J.
pp
la la la la la fa la la la la, With a
RA.
la la la la fa la la la la, With a
ES.
la la la la la la la la, With a
rall.
pp a tempo
ff
Horns
STAND.
sf rall.
fal la lal For Bluff King Hal, Of Eng-land, Merrie Eng - - land!
154-191

F
Allegro giocoso. (♩.=120.)
B.
J.
RA.
ES.
TAILOR.
Hey with a ho With a hey non-ny
BAKER.
Hey with a ho With a hey non-ny
TINKER.
Hey with a ho With a hey
BUTCHER.
Hey with a ho With a hey
CHORUS OF MEN.
Hey with a ho With a hey non-ny
Hey with a ho With a hey
Allegro giocoso. (♩.=120.)
F
Fl. & Ob.

TA.
no non - ny no, With a hey non - ny
BA.
no non - ny no, With a hey non - ny
TI.
oh hey non - ny no, With a hey
BU.
oh hey non - ny no, With a hey
MALE CHORUS.
oh, non - ny no, With a hey non - ny
oh, hey non - ny no, With a hey
f Fl. Ob. & Cl.
TA.
no non - ny no non - ny no non - ny no
BA.
no non - ny no non - ny no non - ny no
TI.
ho, hey non - ny no, hey non - ny no hey non - ny no
BU.
ho, hey non - ny no, hey non - ny no hey non - ny no
MALE CHORUS.
no non - ny no non - ny no non - ny no
ho, hey non - ny no, hey non - ny no hey non - ny no
Fl. Ob. & Cl.

TA.
With a hey non - ny no hey non - ny
BA.
With a hey non - ny no hey non - ny
TI.
With a hey non - ny no hey non - ny
BU.
With a hey non - ny no hey non - ny
MALE CHORUS.
With a hey non - ny no hey non - ny
With a hey non - ny no hey non - ny
pizz.
TA.
no, hey non - ny no hey
BA.
no, hey non - ny no hey
TI.
no, hey non - ny no hey
BU.
no, hey non - ny no hey
MALE CHORUS.
no, hey non - ny no hey
no, hey non - ny no hey
arco

No 13. QUARTET.-(The Tailor, Baker, Tinker, Butcher) and MALE CHORUS.

"THE SUN IN THE HEAVEN."

Note. The Solo parts may be taken by ESSEX.

Allegro giocoso. ♩=120.)
G
THE TAILOR. 1. The sun in the hea-ven is high! No
THE BAKER. 2. clouds they may come in the sky! The
MALE CHORUS.
ho!
ho!
Allegro giocoso. ♩=120.)
sf
Str.
Horn (sus.)
TA.
clouds do be-spec-kle the sky! And a man and a maid Do
rain it may fall by and bye! And the wa-ter may drench The
Trumpet
kiss in the shade, And so shall my bot-tle and I, And
man and the wench, A fig for cold wa-ter, say I, A

The Ladies enter 2 bars before Letter M, and sing the melody to the end.

TA.
so shall my bot-tle and I,
fig for cold wa-ter, say I,
With a hey and a ho! With a
Horns
ALL.
H
hey non-ny no with a hey non-ny no, With a hey non-ny
MALE CHORUS.
And so shall my bot-tle and
A fig for cold wa-ter, say
ten.
animato
ALL.
no, THE TAILOR. A fig for the wea-ther, say I.
THE BAKER. What-ev-er the wea-ther, I'm dry.
I.
I.
Cl. (sus.)
sf pizz.
p
pp
animato
Horn

J
a tempo
Giocoso.
rit.
ALL.
MALE CHORUS.
In
Sum-mer or Win-ter, in
Giocoso.
rit.
sf a tempo
Brass
B. D. & Cym.
Tutti
Au-tumn or Spring. What-ev-er be-tide me What-ev-er they bring, With my
UNIS.
Au-tumn or Spring, What-ev-er be-tide me What-ev-er they bring, my
bot-tle be-side me I'm a-ble to sing, I'm a-ble to sing,
bot-tle be-side me I'm a-ble to sing, I'm a-ble to sing, to

ALL.
My hey non-ny non-ny, my hey non-ny no, My bot-tle be-side me I'm
MALE CHORUS.
My hey non-ny non-ny, my hey non-ny no, My bot-tle be-side me I'm
sing, my hey, ho, hey, ho, hey, ho,
(two high voices.)
(two low voices.)
a-ble to sing, My hey non-ny non-ny My hey non-ny
a-ble to sing, My hey non-ny non-ny My hey non-ny
hey, ho, My hey non-ny non-ny My hey non-ny
K
ENCORE (2nd time.)
1. BAKER.
2. BUTCHER.
no.
The
The
no.
no.
Str.
pp

BU.
snow it may co-ver the ground! The ri-ver with ice may be
p ten.
ten.
meno mosso (con espress.)
bound, But when mai-dens grow old And love grow-eth cold, And
pp colla voce
Horn (sus.)
f a tempo
Tpt.
love grow-eth cold, My bot-tle and I shall be found My
f risoluto
L
BAKER, TINKER, TAILOR & BUTCHER.
f
bot-tle and I shall be found With our hey and our ho! How-
sf

ALL.
-ev-er the sea-sons, how-ev-er the sea-sons, how-ev-er the sea-sons go
round.
rit.
In
M
sf a tempo giocoso.
Sum-mer or Win-ter In
MALE CHORUS.
Brass
B.D. & Cym.
Tutti
Au-tumn or Spring What-ev-er be-tide me What-ev-er they bring, With my
Au-tumn or Spring What-ev-er be-tide me What-ev-er they bring, my

ALL.
bot-tle be-side me I'm a-ble to sing I'm a-ble to
MALE CHORUS.
bot-tle be-side me I'm a-ble to sing I'm a-ble to
bot-tle be-side me I'm a-ble to sing I'm a-ble to
ALL.
sing, My hey non-ny non-ny, my hey non-ny no, My
MALE CHORUS.
sing, My hey non-ny non-ny, my hey non-ny no, My
sing, to sing My hey, ho, hey, ho,
ALL
bot-tle be-side me I'm a-ble to sing, My hey non-ny
MALE CHORUS.
bot-tle be-side me I'm a-ble to sing, My hey non-ny
hey ho hey ho, My hey non-ny

O
a tempo
rall.
ALL.
non-ny my hey non-ny no.
MALE CHORUS.
non-ny my hey non-ny no.
non-ny my hey non-ny no.
rall.
a tempo
Tutti
ALL.
MALE CHORUS.
ff
Tamb.
accel.
pizz.
sf
sf

No. 14. DUET.–(Jill and Raleigh.)

"IT IS THE MERRY MONTH OF MAY"

Allegretto. ♩= 126.
JILL.
Semplice. Fl. (trem.)
p
Str.
It is the mer-ry month of May, The bees do hum a roun-de-lay, And all
the world, all the world is sun-ny; So let your brown thoughts
Ob.
A
animato
pp
hie a-way And search the world for hon-ey, And search the
Fl.
pp
f

rit.
a tempo
J.
world for hon-ey!
RALEIGH.
rit.
a tempo
Ah! Love it is a hap-py thing, It com - eth un-to
Ob.
Cl.
rit.
p
a tempo
Hrn.
R.
clown or king, As an-y one may see, As an-y one may
B
R.
see. And of all places where it flies, There is no place be-
Hrn.(sus.)
R.
-neath the skies More fair than where the bracken grows, The honey-suc-kle

R
and the rose, Be-neath the green-wood tree, While bees do hum their
Fl.
pp
R
roun-de-lay. 'Tis there I'll dream that
f
cresc.
Brass
R
love some day May e-ven come to me!
W.W.
Vio.1.
f animato
JILL.
ENCORE.
rit.
That love may come to me!
RALEIGH.
R
rit.
Oh!
cresc.
ff
rit.
Brass

C
J.
It is the mer-ry month of May; The bees do hum a roun-de-lay And
R.
Love it is a hap-py thing, It com - eth un-to clown or king
p a tempo
Triang.
J.
all the world, all the world is sun-ny: Oh!
R.
As an-y one may see, as an-y one may see.
animato
pp
J.
Love oh! Love it is a hap-py thing, It
R.
And of all pla-ces where it flies, There is no place be-

J.
com - eth un-to clown or king, un-to
R.
-neath the skies More fair than where the brack-en grows,
J.
clown or king. Broader Be - neath, beneath the
R.
The ho-ney-suc-kle, and the rose, More fair than where
colla voce.
Hrn.
Largamente.
D
J.
green - wood tree Where bees do hum their roun-de-lay. 'Tis there I'll dream that
R.
the bracken grows. 'Tis there 'tis there I'll dream that
D
colla voce
Tutti

J.
R.
Love may e-ven come to me, may e-ven come to me, That
Love may e-ven come to me, may come to me, 'Tis
Str. (sus.)
Fl. & Cl.
love may come to me. 'Tis there I'll dream that
there I'll dream that love, that love may come to me, that
Cl.
mf p rall.
love may come to me!
love may come to me!
Fl.
Cl.
mf Str.
p colla voce
pp
Ped.

No. 15. RUSTIC DANCE and JIG.

Allegro moderato. ♩. = 112
Str.
L
f Tutti
p
Ped. Timp.
Ped.
f
p
pp delicato
M

Tutti
f
Ob.
Cl.
f p
f p
f p
1.
2.
rit.
p
a tempo.
O
Ped.
*
Ped.
*
Ped.
*

f
p
f
p
f
Ped.
dim molto
P
delicato.
ppp
Tutti
ff
accel.
ENCORE.
Prestissimo. ♩= 200.
Str.
ff trem.
ff
Tamb.
JIG.
Str. & W.W.
sf
p

R
tr
f
p
S
Tutti

Ob.
p
f
Ped.
*
Tutti
U
V (2nd time)
tr
1.
V

2.
Tutti
ff
sf
Timp.
Ped.
8
*
animato
accel.
sempre
pizz.
arco
Segue.

Nº 16. SONG.–(Raleigh.)

"THE ENGLISH ROSE!"

Andantino. ♩= 80.
mf
(Beat 2)
Str. W. W. & Hrns.
dim.
RALEIGH.
Dan Cu-pid hath a gar - den Where women are the
p
pp
(Beat quick 4)
flow'rs,— And lov-ers' laughs and lov-ers' tears, The sun-shine and the
show'rs — And Oh! the sweet - est
A
W. W. (sus.)

blos - som That in the gar - den grows The
cresc.
f
fair - est Queen, it is, I ween, The per - fect Eng - lish rose, The
cresc.
Largamente.
fair - est Queen, it is I ween, The per - fect, the per - fect
f Hrn. Solo
colla voce
p
B
Eng - lish rose!
ENCORE.
Tempo I°
mf
Cello (Beat 2)

Let others make a garland Of
pp
(Beat quick 4)
ev - 'ry flow'r that blows! But I will wait till
I may pluck My dainty English rose
C
In per - fume, grace, and beau - ty The
Vio.1. 8ve.

rose doth stand a - part, God grant that I be -
- fore I die May wear one on my heart God
Largamente.
ff
grant that I be - fore I die May wear one, may
colla voce
p Str.
Hrn. Solo
wear one on my heart.
pp
ppp

→ p183

No 17. DUET.—(Essex and Raleigh.) and CHORUS.

Allegro giocoso. ♩ = 108.
f
Tutti
Animato. ♩. = 138.
A
ESSEX.
1. Two mer-ry men a-drink-ing, a-drink-ing! Be-fore the moon was sink-ing, a-sink-ing! A Strang-er he did pass that way, And
2. As Ro-bin lay a-think-ing, a-think-ing, And Tuck, did sit a drink-ing, a-drink-ing, The Strang-er he did stout-ly say
Cl.
dim.
pp
ES.
Triang.
Hrn.

ES.
he did lis - ten to their lay; And he did lis - ten to their
This is a game that two can play; This is a game that two can
ES.
lay;
play;
pp
CHORUS.
All on a sum - mer's night, all on a
pp
All on a sum - mer's night, all on a
pp
Fl. & Cl.
B
RALEIGH.
rall.
a tempo
Ah! Who dares to drink Or
CHORUS.
sum - mer's night.
sum - mer's night.
♩ = 108.
a tempo
rall.
p
Trumpet.
S. Drum.
Brass

C
R.
fight with me, I'll not shrink Who-ev-er he be, I'll crack his crown Or
Str.
rall.
a tempo
drink him down Be-fore the grey of morn-ing, O!
CHORUS.
He'll crack his crown, Or
He'll crack his crown, Or
W.W.
sf
Tutti
2 verses
Back to 170
drink him down Be - fore the grey of morn - ing!
drink him down Be - fore the grey of morn - ing!
Animato.(♩. = 138.)

D
ESSEX.
Then Tuck he stood a-blink-ing a-blink-ing
dim.
pp
ES.
At Ro-bin Hood a-wink-ing, a-wink-ing, And
ES
Tuck did to the Strang-er say "To Ro-bin Hood there's toll to pay, To
ES.
f
Ro-bin Hood there's toll, there's toll to
pizz.

pay!"
CHORUS.
All on a Summer's night, All
All on a Summer's night, All
Brass
E
Prestissimo.
on a Sum - mer's night!
on a Sum - mer's night!
Prestissimo.
Cymb. with wooden end of stick.
ROBIN HOOD and LITTLE JOHN fight with staves.
Brass

W.W.
Ped.
tr
sf
sff
Fag. & Cello
Str.

F Meno mosso. ♩. = 92.
ESSEX.
Poor Ro-bin lay a think-ing, a think-ing! And Tuck he sat a blink-ing, a blink-ing. And
dim.
p
Ob. & Hrn.
Fag:
f
S. Drum.
♩. = 138.
Lit-tle John did sing this lay, For he it was who won the day,
mf animato
Brass (p)
Who won the day,
pp
All on a Sum-mer's night, All on a
CHORUS.
pp
All on a Sum-mer's night, All on a
pp
ES.

ES.
rall.
Sum-mer's night.
Sum-mer's night.
mf
rall.
Ped.
G
RALEIGH. with SOPRANI.
CHORUS.
Then all did sit a drink-ing, a
ESSEX. with BASSI.
Then all did sit a drink-ing, a
ENCORE.
f a tempo
Tutti
drink-ing Un-til the moon was sink-ing, a sink-ing
drink-ing Un-til the moon was sink-ing, a sink-ing
Triang.

— For Lit - tle John did with them stay, So all did sing this
— For Lit - tle John did with them stay, So all did sing this
RALEIGH.
Not too fast.
round - e - lay! So all did sing this round - e -
ESSEX.
round - e - lay! So all did sing this round - e -
So all did sing this round - e -
ALTO
round - e - lay! So all did sing, did sing this round - e -
CHORUS.
So all did sing this round - e -
round - e - lay! So all did sing this round - e - lay this round - e -
Not too fast.
W.W.

R.
ES.
CHORUS.
-lay, For all did sing For all did sing this
-lay, For all did sing this round-e-lay, For all did
-lay, For all did sing For all did sing this
-lay, did sing this round-e-lay this
-lay, For all did sing this round-e-lay For all did
-lay, all did sing this
round-e-lay! On ma-ny a Sum-mer's
sing this round-e-lay! On ma-ny a Sum-mer's
round-e-lay! Up-on
round-e-lay! On ma-ny a. Sum-mer's
sing this round-e-lay! On
round-e-lay! On ma-ny a. Sum-mer's

H
rall.
♩= 108.
a tempo
R.
ES.
ff
night. Who_ dares to drink or fight with me,
rall.
ff
a tempo
Trumpet
S. Drum
Brass
RALEIGH. with SOPRANI.
I
drink him down,
I'll not shrink Who - ever he be, I'll crack his crown, Or drink him down,
ESSEX. with BASSI.
I'll not shrink Who - ever he be, I'll crack his crown, Or drink him down,

rall.
a tempo
Be - fore the grey of morn-ing O!
drink him down! I'll crack his crown, Or
rall.
drink him down! I'll crack his crown, Or
rall.
sf
a tempo
Tutti
Be - fore the
drink him down Be - fore the grey of morn - ing, Be - fore the grey of
drink him down Be - fore the grey of morn - ing, I'll
Broader.
morn - ing, I'll crack his crown, or drink him down, be -
crack his crown I'll crack his crown, or drink him down, be -
Broader.

Presto
R.
-fore the grey of morn - - - ing.
ES.
-fore the grey of morn - - - ing.
-fore the grey of morn - - - ing.
-fore the grey of morn - - - ing.
Presto
sff
R.
ES.
pizz.
arco

Nº 18. SONG.—(Bessie.)

SIT

Molto allegro à la Valse. ♩ = 88.
Str.
Cl.
p
Hrn.(sus.)
O — who shall say that Love is cru - el! I do guard it as a jew - el, Count - ing it — a sin - gle flow - er In a world of weed. — O —
A
what if Love do bring me sor - row; Love to - day, — and
rit.
f
Ob.
Brass (pp)

a tempo
die to - mor - row. Love-less life is life - less liv - ing; That were
a tempo
p
B
death in - deed.
animato
Fl.
Slow.
f
a tempo
p
Life is sweet, but Love is sweet-er,
f
p
Brass
B. D.
Str.
Slow.
a tempo
Life is prose, but Love a me-tre.
f
p
Brass
B. D.
Str.

C
Throb-bing with the pulse of mu - sic, All that Lov - ers need,
p
Throb-bing with the pulse of mu - sic, All that Lov - ers
Hrns.
D pp Fl.
need. Life's a chime and Love the ring-er, Life's a
pp
lute and Love the sing-er, Tho' he choose a song of

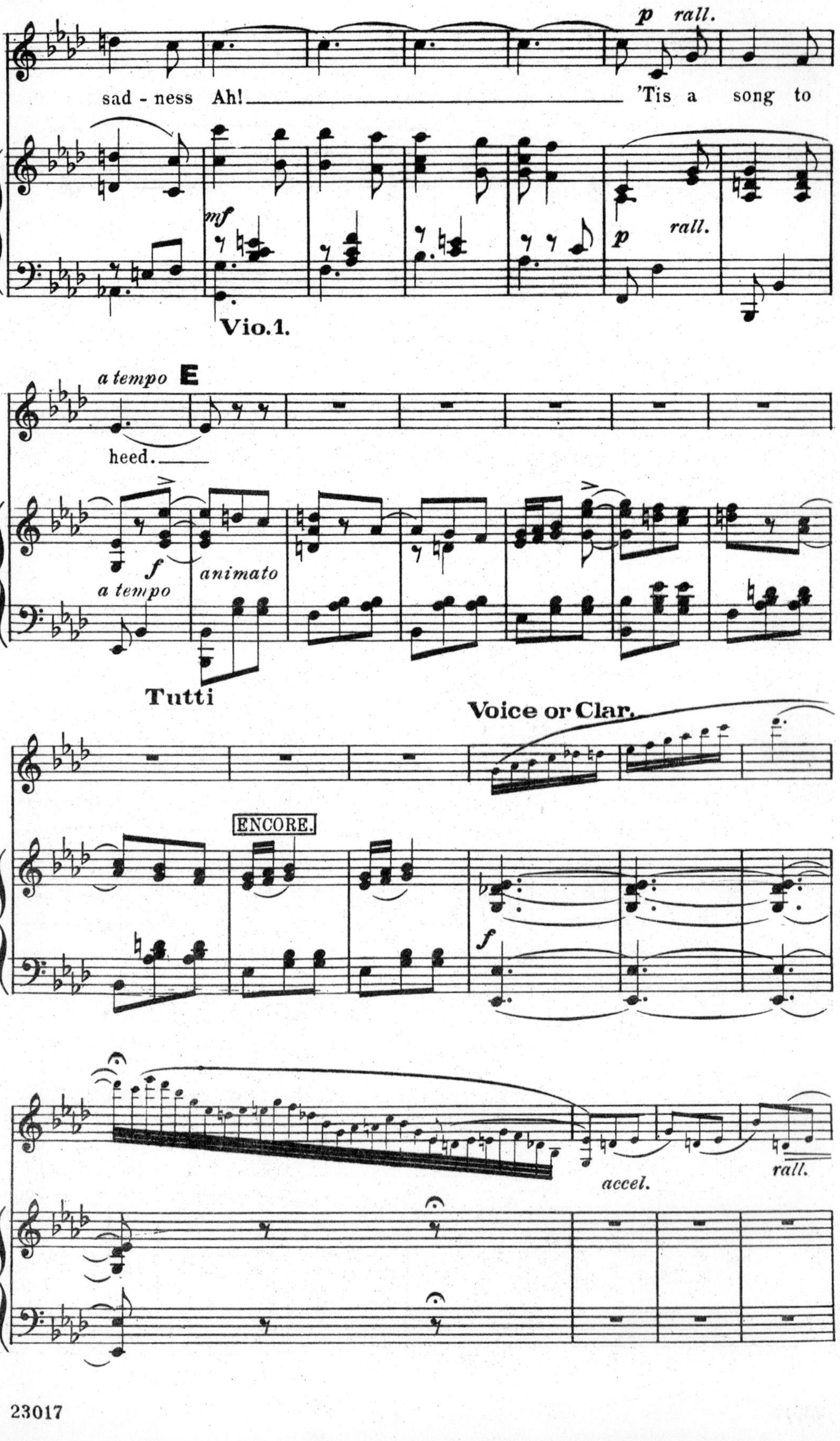
p rall.
sad - ness Ah! 'Tis a song to
mf
p rall.
Vio.1.
a tempo E
heed.
f
a tempo
animato
Tutti
Voice or Clar.
ENCORE.
f
accel.
rall.

J a tempo
O — Life's the can - vas; nought is dull - er Till it
Cl.
p
Str.
glow-eth gay with col-our, 'Neath the hand of Love the Paint-er,
Fl. K
Mas-ter of de-sign. — O — Love-less Life is life-less
frit.
a tempo
liv - ing, On - ly Love — hath pow'r of giv - ing Un - to
frit.
f
a tempo
Ob.

Life its breath and beau - - - ty.
accel. poco - - - a - - - poco
f animato
Love, love is all di - vine, Love is all di -
Brass
- vine, Love is all, is all di - vine.
sf
ff
sf
Molto Allegro
Brass
Tutti
sf
sf
sf

To p. 198

No. 19. SONG.-(Essex.)

(with Bessie, Jill and Raleigh.)

ENCORE.
Allegro spiritoso. ♩= 112.
(Not too fast.)
Brillante.
ff
Tutti
Str.
ten.
Hrn.
ESSEX.
A
When Cu-pid first this old world trod, He was you know, a
-neath my La-dy Fash-ion's rule Poor Cu-pid then was
Cu-pid sel-dom comes to us "In pu-ris na-tu-
delicato
pp
ES.
Cl.
ba-by god; And old Dame Na-ture nurs'd the lad, But let him run a-
sent to school, And learn'd the laws of com-mon-sense, And how to val-ue
-ra-li-bus;" For such ex-treme-ly sim-ple guise Would shock the mo-dern

BESSIE.
JILL.
ppp
And old Dame Na - ture nursed the lad, But let him
And learned the laws of com - mon sense, And how to
For such ex - treme - ly sim - ple guise Would shock the
RALEIGH.
ppp
And old Dame Na - ture nursed the lad, But let him
And learned the laws of com - mon sense, And how to
For such ex - treme - ly sim - ple guise Would shock the
ES.
- bout un - clad.
pounds and pence.
world - ly - wise!
ppp
ten.
Fl. & Picc.
B
J
run a - bout un - clad.
val - ue pounds and pence.
mo - dern world - ly - wise!
ESSEX.
B
One day my La - dy
She dressed him up from
Yet e - ven now some -
R
run a - bout un - clad.
val - ue pounds and pence.
mo - dern world - ly - wise!
p
ES.
Fash - ion came, And blushed be - neath her rouge with shame, To see the pret - ty
toe _ to top, And put him in a Lon - don shop, Where Cu - pid, at the
times they say, He takes a lit - tle hol - i - day, And ev - 'ry now and

BESSIE.
ppp
JILL.
To see the
Where Cu - pid,
And ev - 'ry
RALEIGH.
ppp
To see the
Where Cupid,
And ev - 'ry
ES.
in - no-cent Un - clothed in Gip-sy Na-tures tent.
coun-ter sells New tunes for mo-dern mar-riage bells.
then re-turns Where old Dame Na-ture waits and yearns!
ten.
ppp
ten.
Fl.
B.
J.
pret-ty in - no-cent Un-clothed in Gip-sy Na-ture's tent.
at the coun-ter sells New tunes for mo-dern mar-riage bells.
now and then re-turns Where old Dame Na-ture waits and yearns!
R.
pret-ty in - no-cent Un-clothed in Gip-sy Na ture's tent.
at the coun-ter sells New tunes for mo-dern mar-riage bells.
now and then re-turns Where old Dame Na-ture waits and yearns!
Str.

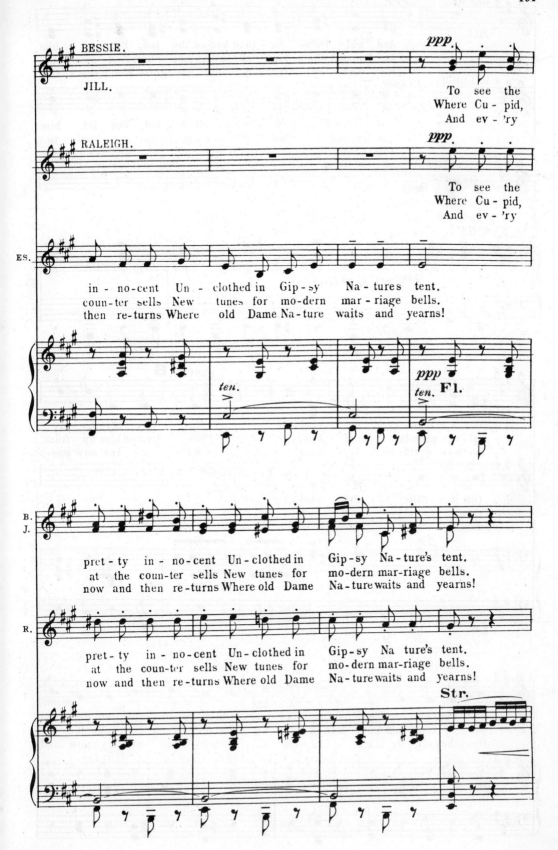

ESSEX.
C
And, heed-less of Dame Na-ture's curse, She
For Love no lon-ger baits his hooks With
For Love's a Gip-sy still at heart, Tho'
Fl. (8ve)
pp
took him from his Gip-sy nurse, And set him in her
gen-tle sighs and ten-der looks, But now a-days poor
fash-ion makes him look so smart: And I, for one, would
Cl. (sus.)
Ob.
cha-ri-ot, De-ter-mined to im-prove his lot.
lo-vers get En-tan-gled by a mil-lion net.
not complain Were he a na-ked child a-gain!
Vio. 1.

D
BESSIE.
JILL.
And heed-less of Dame Na-ture's curse, She took him from his
For Love no lon-ger baits his hooks With gen-tle sighs and
For Love's a Gip-sy still at heart, Tho' fash-ion makes him
RALEIGH.
And heed less of Dame Na-ture's curse, She took him from his
For Love no lon-ger baits his hooks With gen-tle sighs and
For Loves a Gip-sy still at heart, Tho' fash-ion makes him
ES.
fp
Triang.
her cha - ri-ot,
poor lov - ers get,
would not complain,
rall.
a tempo
pp
B.
J.
Gip-sy nurse, And set him in her cha - ri - ot, And
ten-der looks, But now-a-days poor lov - ers get, But
look so smart: And I, for one, would not com - plain, And
R.
Gip-sy nurse, And set him in her cha - ri - ot, And
ten-der looks, But now-a-days poor lov - ers get, But
look so smart: And I, for one, would not com - plain, And
ES.
And set him in her cha - ri - ot, And
But now-a-days poor lov - ers get, But
And I, for one, would not com - plain, And

ppp (rall. & pause last time only) 1 & 2.
B.
J.
set him in her cha-ri-ot, De-ter-mined to im-prove his lot.
now-a-days poor lov-ers get En-tan-gled by a mil-lion net.
I, for one, would not complain Were he a na-ked child a-
ppp
R.
set him in her cha-ri-ot, De-ter-mined to im-prove his lot.
now-a-days poor lov-ers get En-tan-gled by a mil-lion net.
I, for one, would not complain Were he a na-ked child a-
ppp
ES.
set him in her cha-ri-ot, De-ter-mined to im-prove his lot.
now-a-days poor lov-ers get En-tan-gled by a mil-lion net.
I, for one, would not complain Were he a na-ked child a-
1 & 2.
ppp
(rall. & pause last time only)
ff a tempo
Tutti
Str.
ten.
ESSEX
2. Be-
3. So
dim

Last time.
B.
J.
gain!
R.
gain!
ES.
gain!
Str.
ppp delicato
Brillante
ff Tutti
pizz.
sf
Ped.

SEGUE FINALE.

STAND

Nº 20. FINALE – ACT II.

Allegro. ♩.=88.
BESSIE & RALEIGH.
"Now
ff
Tutti
B. & R.
who'll come," Said Ro-bin Hood, "Who'll come to my wed-ding?"
mf Str.
pp
Hrn. (sus.)
JILL.
All those who love The blue sky a - bove,
ten.
J.
And the green grass to lie up-on. 'Tis bet-ter than bed-ding!

BESSIE & RALEIGH.
J.
CHORUS.
O all such are wel-come at Ro-bin Hood's wed-ding. And
O all are wel - come all are wel-come.
Tutti
A
B & R
who'll tie the lov-er's knot At Ro-bin Hood's wed-ding?
mf Str.
pp
Hrn. (sus.)
ESSEX.
"I," said the Friar, "And I'll lead the choir,"
ten.
ES.
Quoth Fri-ar Tuck to Ro-bin Hood at Ro-bin Hood's wed-ding.
pp

BESSE & RALEIGH.
ES.
CHORUS.
Quoth Fri-ar Tuck to Ro-bin Hood at Ro-bin Hood's wed-ding. And
Quoth Fri - ar Tuck to Ro - bin Hood.
Tutti
B
B & R
who'll be the groom his man At Ro-bin Hood's wed-ding?
mf Str.
pp
Hrn.(sus.)
ESSEX.
"I," said Big John, "My Lin-coln I'll don,"
ten.
ES.
Quoth Lit-tle John to Ro-bin Hood At Ro-bin Hood's wed-ding.

BESSIE & RALEIGH.
ES.
CHORUS.
all
Quoth Lit-tle John to Ro-bin Hood at Ro-bin Hood's wed-ding. And
Quoth Lit - tle John to Ro - bin Hood.
Tutti
E
B & R
who'll give the bride a-way At Ro-bin Hood's wed-ding?
mf Str.
pp
Hrn. (sus.)
ESSEX.
"I," said the King, "My Queen, too, I bring.
ten.
Quoth Rich-ard un - to Ro-bin Hood At Ro-bin Hood's wed-ding.

RALEIGH.
ES.
CHORUS.
Quoth Richard un - to Ro-bin Hood At Ro-bin Hood's wedding. And
Quoth Rich - ard un - to Ro - bin Hood.
Tutti
F
R.
Who'll dance with Ro-bin Hood At Ro-bin Hood's wed-ding?
Str.
Hrn.(sus.)
BESSIE.
"I," said his bride, "I'll dance by thy side."
ten.
B.
Quoth Ma-ri-on to Ro-bin Hood At Ro-bin Hood's wed-ding

B.
TUTTI.
CHORUS.
f
Quoth Ma-ri-on to Ro-bin Hood At Ro-bin Hood's wedding. Then
f
Quoth Ma - ri - on to Ro - bin Hood. Then
f
G
pomposo
fff
God save the King, And God save the Queen!
fff
God save the King, And God save the Queen!
pomposo
fff
Tutti
And let us all sing And dance on the
And let us all sing And dance on the

green, ____ In me-mo-ry of Ro-bin Hood, In me-mo-ry of Ma-rion
green, ____ In me - mo - ry of Ro - bin Hood And
Str. Fl. & Ob.
And all the mer-ry men and maids Who danced at their wed-ding__
all of the merry mer-ry men Who danced at their wed-ding__
Triang.
Tpts.
With a hey! With a hey! With a
With a hey! With a hey!

H
B. J.
R.
ES.
CHORUS.
rall. molto
fff
With a
sempre cresc.
hey!
With a hey!
Brass.
a tempo
hey, Ro - bin, jol - ly, jol - ly Ro - bin, Hey, Ro - bin,
fff a tempo
Tutti

B.
J.
jol - ly, jol - ly Ro - bin, Thou'lt wear a crown a
R.
jol - ly, jol - ly Ro - bin, Thou'lt wear a crown a
ES.
jol - ly, jol - ly Ro - bin, Thou'lt wear a crown a
CHORUS.
jol - ly, jol - ly Ro - bin, Thou'lt wear a crown a
jol - ly, jol - ly Ro - bin, Thou'lt wear a crown a
long pause
Allegro brillante.
king may ne - ver see!
king may ne - ver see!
king may ne - ver see!
king may ne - ver see!
king may ne - ver see!
long pause Allegro brillante.
ff

B.D. & Cymb.

accel
er
an
do
Timp.
ff
sf
pizz.
arco
long pause
sff
Ped.
*

Lowe and Brydone (Printers) Limited, London

FINE.

TOM JONES

A Comic Opera in Three Acts

Founded on Fielding's Novel by A. M. THOMPSON and ROBERT COURTNEIDGE

LYRICS BY
CHAS. H. TAYLOR

MUSIC BY
EDWARD GERMAN

CHAPPELL & CO. Ltd. 50 NEW BOND STREET, LONDON, W.1
NEW YORK · TORONTO · SYDNEY · PARIS

No. 257

Y

THE REBEL MAID

A Romantic Light Opera.

Book by
ALEX. M. THOMPSON and GERALD DODSON.

Lyrics by
GERALD DODSON.

Music by
MONTAGUE F. PHILLIPS.

Vocal Score (Complete.)
Vocal Score (Concert Version.)

Separate **VOCAL NUMBERS** *may be had as follows:*

THE FISHERMEN OF ENGLAND (In B♭ and C)
SAIL MY SHIPS
ARE MY LANTERNS SHINING?
WHEN A DREAM OF LOVE YOU CHERISH
THE OLD-FASHIONED CLOAK
HOME AGAIN
SHEPHERDESS AND BEAU BROCADE. (Quartet) S.A.T.B.
HOW STRANGE THIS TUMULT. (Madrigal) S.A.T.B
WISDOM AND FOLLY. (Unaccompanied Madrigal) S.A.T.B.

PIANOFORTE ARRANGEMENTS.

THE REBEL MAID VALSE
THE REBEL MAID GAVOTTE
THE REBEL MAID SELECTION
FOUR DANCES from "The Rebel Maid." (Arranged by the Composer).

CHAPPELL & CO., LTD.,
50, NEW BOND STREET, LONDON, W.1.
NEW YORK. SYDNEY.
And may be had of all Music Sellers.

No. 213